BRIEF ATLAS
OF THE
HUMAN BODY

Kevin T. Patton, PhD
Professor of Life Sciences
St. Charles Community College
Cottleville, Missouri

Gary A. Thibodeau, PhD
Chancellor Emeritus and Professor Emeritus of Biology
University of Wisconsin—River Falls
River Falls, Wisconsin

MOSBY

ELSEVIER

LEARNING AND INFORMATION
SERVICES
UNIVERSITY OF CUMBRIA

MOSBY
ELSEVIER

11830 Westline Industrial Drive
St. Louis, Missouri 63146

BRIEF ATLAS OF THE HUMAN BODY FOR
ANATOMY & PHYSIOLOGY, 7th EDITION

ISBN/Part Number: 9996057763

ISBN/Part Number 9996057763

Executive Publisher: Tom Wilhelm
Acquistions Editor: Jeff Downing
Developmental Editor: Karen C. Turner
Associate Developmental Editor: Jennifer Hermes
Editorial Assistant: Jennifer Shropshire
Publishing Services Manager: Deborah L. Vogel
Senior Project Manager: Deon Lee
Cover Design Direction: Paula Catalano

Printed in the United States of America

Last digit is the print number: 9 8 7 6 5 4 3 2 1

Contents

PART 3   INTERNAL ANATOMY   53

PART 4   CROSS-SECTIONAL ANATOMY   67

PART 5   HISTOLOGY   79

Introduction to the Brief Atlas of the Human Body

During our many years of teaching anatomy and physiology, we have found that supplemental images of body structures often help students appreciate the "big picture" of human anatomy and physiology. For that reason, we wanted to provide some of these images in a handy supplement to *Anatomy & Physiology* to help you with your learning.

This *Brief Atlas* contains images from some of the world's best medical atlases. It provides a manageable overview of the human body in an easy-to-use size and format. You will find it helpful for learning in both the lecture/discussion part of the course and in the laboratory part of your anatomy and physiology course.

Part 1, *Surface Anatomy*, provides a brief overview of the surface structures of the body. Notice that many of these images feature the locations of major structures that lie just under the skin. These underlying structures include bones, muscles, and various other internal organs. These images will help you understand the relationship of the internal organs to the surface view of the body.

Part 2, *The Skeleton*, features a number of detailed photographs of the human skeleton. These images include many views of the different regions of the human skeleton and of individual bones of the skeleton. You will find these to be useful references as you study the bones and muscles of the body.

Part 3, *Internal Anatomy*, provides a survey of helpful images of the inside structures of the body. These images often include representations of dissected organs of many different systems to help you see how they all fit together in the human body. We have also included some casts, images produced by filling up hollow body structures (such as blood vessels) with a substance that hardens to produce a molded casting of what the hollow spaces look like. Such casts help you appreciate body structure in a different way than ordinary anatomical images.

Part 4, *Cross-Sectional Anatomy*, features an introductory set of horizontal sections of the human body. Such sectional views help you develop a stronger sense of the three-dimensional relationships of the various structures of the body. Because of the increasing importance of cross-sectional anatomy in today's medical imaging, we believe that this resource is especially useful in helping you apply your understanding of human body structure in practical, applied ways.

Part 5, *Histology*, is a miniatlas of some of the major types of tissues found in the body. Our experience as students and teachers tells us that an understanding of tissues, or histology, is a good foundation for easily learning the anatomy of every part of the body. Our experience also tells us that the more examples you see early in your studies, the easier it is to grasp the fundamental concepts of histology. So this section of the *Brief Atlas* provides a handy set of tissue samples gleaned from the major histology atlases to supplement those already found in *Anatomy & Physiology*, 7th Edition.

We trust that you will find these carefully selected images helpful in your study of human anatomy and physiology!

Kevin T. Patton
Gary A. Thibodeau

PART 1

Surface Anatomy

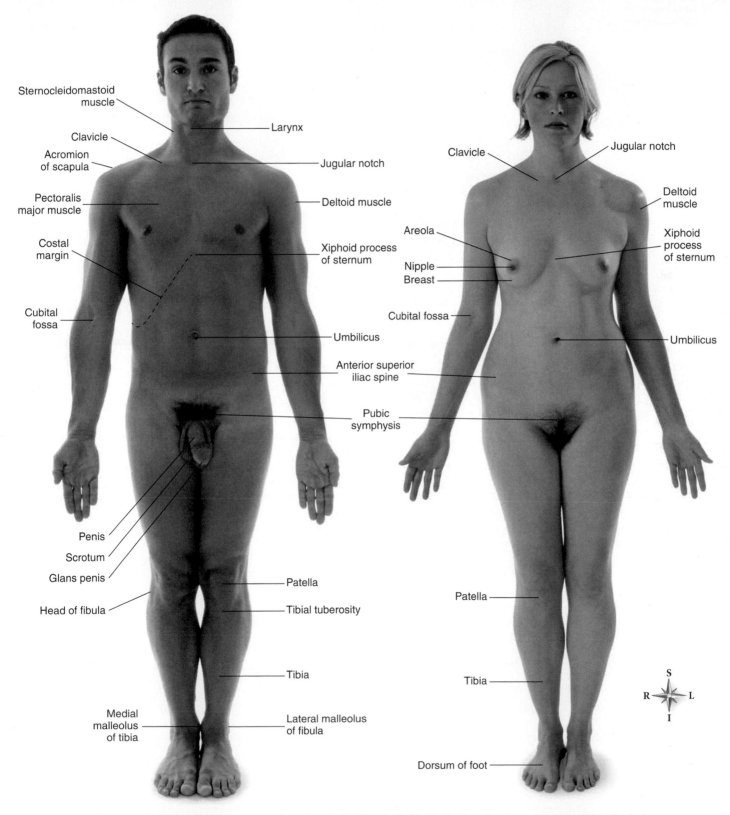

Figure 1-1 *Overview of surface anatomy (anterior view).* (From Drake RL: *Gray's atlas of anatomy,* New York, 2008, Elsevier.)

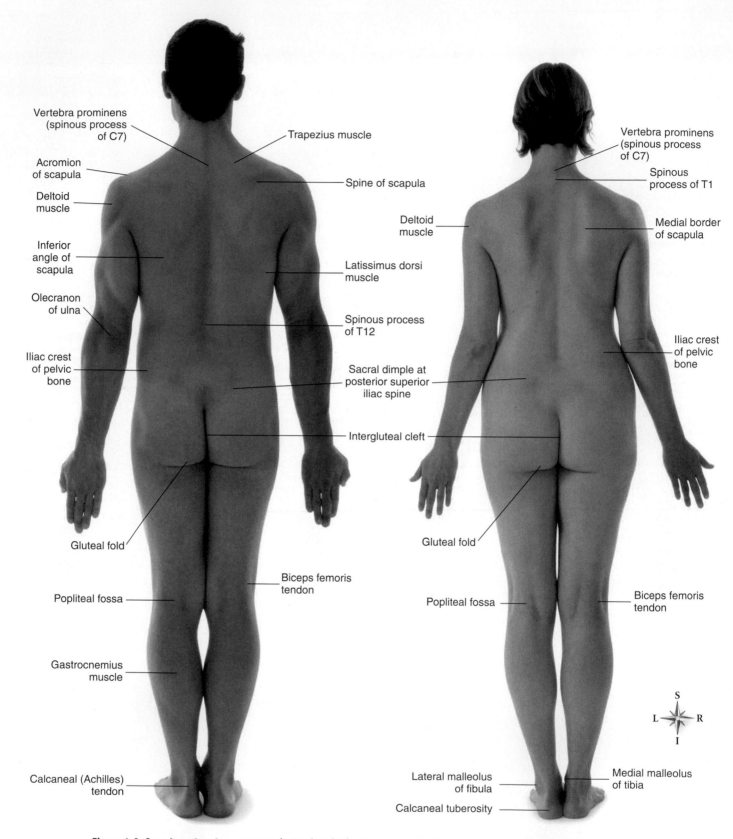

Vertebra prominens (spinous process of C7)

Trapezius muscle

Acromion of scapula

Spine of scapula

Deltoid muscle

Inferior angle of scapula

Latissimus dorsi muscle

Olecranon of ulna

Spinous process of T12

Iliac crest of pelvic bone

Sacral dimple at posterior superior iliac spine

Intergluteal cleft

Gluteal fold

Biceps femoris tendon

Popliteal fossa

Gastrocnemius muscle

Calcaneal (Achilles) tendon

Vertebra prominens (spinous process of C7)

Spinous process of T1

Deltoid muscle

Medial border of scapula

Iliac crest of pelvic bone

Gluteal fold

Popliteal fossa

Biceps femoris tendon

Lateral malleolus of fibula

Medial malleolus of tibia

Calcaneal tuberosity

Figure 1-2 *Overview of surface anatomy (posterior view).* (From Drake RL: *Gray's atlas of anatomy,* New York, 2008, Elsevier.)

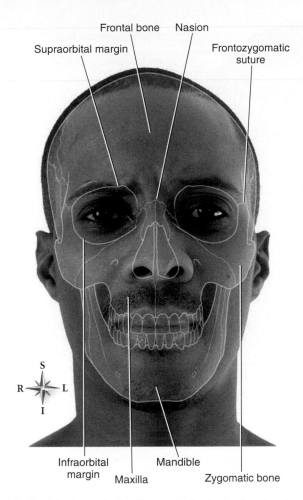

Figure 1-3 *Head (anterior view).* (From Drake RL: *Gray's atlas of anatomy,* New York, 2008, Elsevier.)

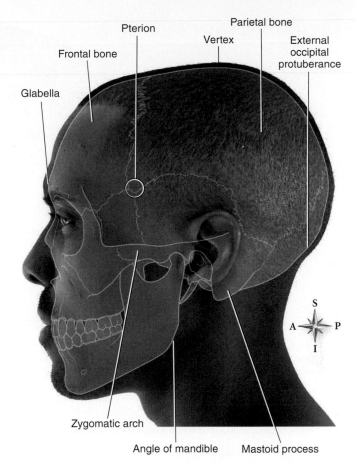

Figure 1-4 *Head (lateral view).* (From Drake RL: *Gray's atlas of anatomy,* New York, 2008, Elsevier.)

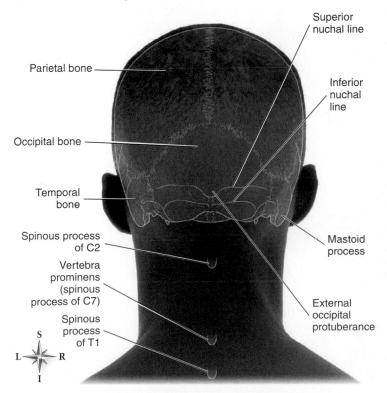

Figure 1-5 *Head (posterior view).* (From Drake RL: *Gray's atlas of anatomy,* New York, 2008, Elsevier.)

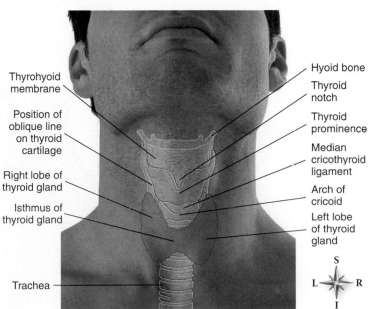

Figure 1-6 *Neck (anterior view).* (From Drake RL: *Gray's atlas of anatomy,* New York, 2008, Elsevier.)

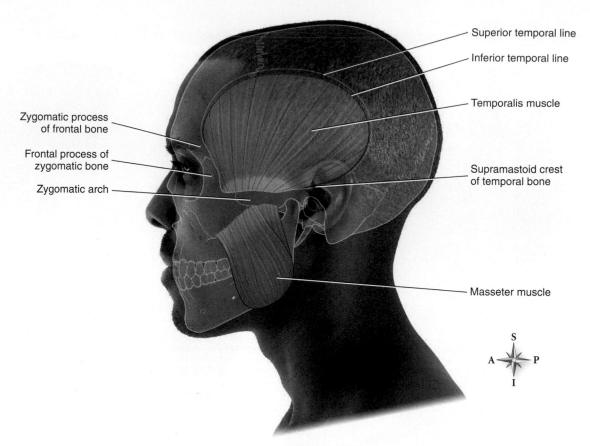

Superior temporal line

Inferior temporal line

Temporalis muscle

Zygomatic process
of frontal bone

Frontal process of
zygomatic bone

Zygomatic arch

Supramastoid crest
of temporal bone

Masseter muscle

Figure 1-7 *Head and neck (left lateral view).* (From Drake RL: *Gray's atlas of anatomy,* New York, 2008, Elsevier.)

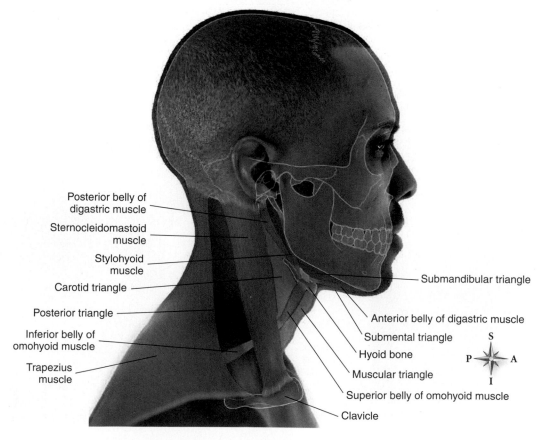

Posterior belly of
digastric muscle

Sternocleidomastoid
muscle

Stylohyoid
muscle

Carotid triangle

Posterior triangle

Inferior belly of
omohyoid muscle

Trapezius
muscle

Submandibular triangle

Anterior belly of digastric muscle

Submental triangle

Hyoid bone

Muscular triangle

Superior belly of omohyoid muscle

Clavicle

Figure 1-8 *Head and neck (right lateral view).* (From Drake RL: *Gray's atlas of anatomy,* New York, 2008, Elsevier.)

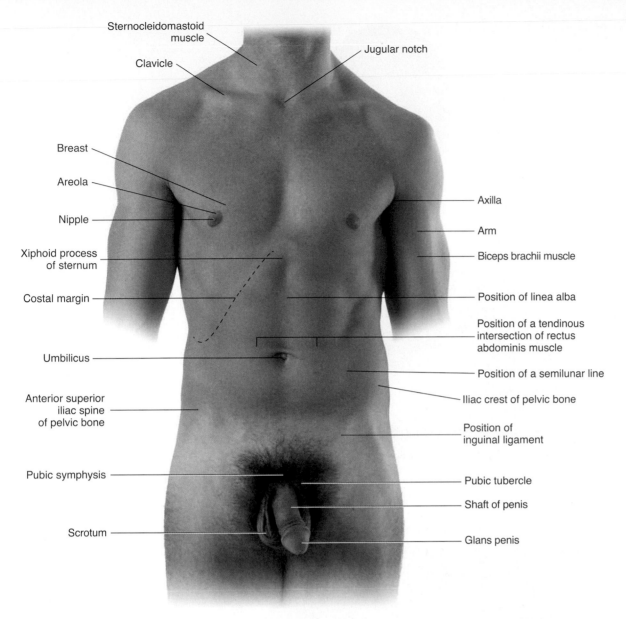

Sternocleidomastoid muscle

Clavicle

Jugular notch

Breast

Areola

Nipple

Xiphoid process of sternum

Costal margin

Umbilicus

Anterior superior iliac spine of pelvic bone

Pubic symphysis

Scrotum

Axilla

Arm

Biceps brachii muscle

Position of linea alba

Position of a tendinous intersection of rectus abdominis muscle

Position of a semilunar line

Iliac crest of pelvic bone

Position of inguinal ligament

Pubic tubercle

Shaft of penis

Glans penis

Figure 1-9 *Male trunk (anterior view)*. (From Drake RL: *Gray's atlas of anatomy,* New York, 2008, Elsevier.)

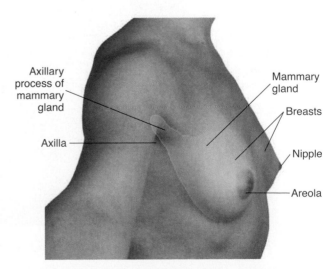

Axillary process of mammary gland

Axilla

Mammary gland

Breasts

Nipple

Areola

Figure 1-10 *Female thorax (right lateral view)*. (From Drake RL: *Gray's atlas of anatomy,* New York, 2008, Elsevier.)

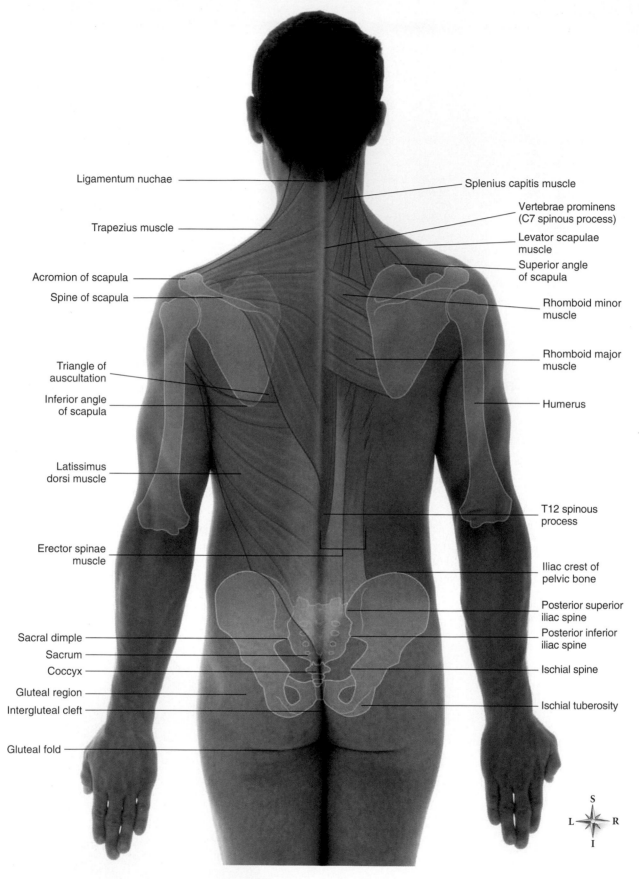

Ligamentum nuchae

Trapezius muscle

Acromion of scapula

Spine of scapula

Triangle of auscultation

Inferior angle of scapula

Latissimus dorsi muscle

Erector spinae muscle

Sacral dimple

Sacrum

Coccyx

Gluteal region

Intergluteal cleft

Gluteal fold

Splenius capitis muscle

Vertebrae prominens (C7 spinous process)

Levator scapulae muscle

Superior angle of scapula

Rhomboid minor muscle

Rhomboid major muscle

Humerus

T12 spinous process

Iliac crest of pelvic bone

Posterior superior iliac spine

Posterior inferior iliac spine

Ischial spine

Ischial tuberosity

S

L — R

I

Figure 1-11 *Surface of trunk (posterior view).* (From Drake RL: *Gray's atlas of anatomy,* New York, 2008, Elsevier.)

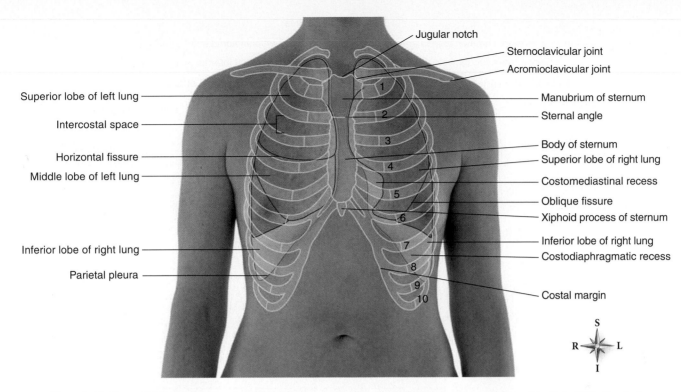

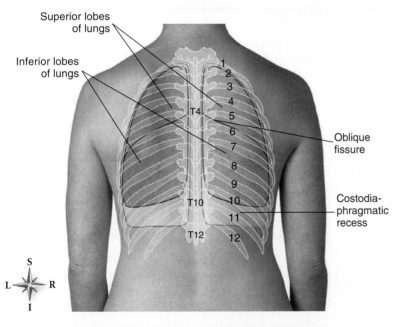

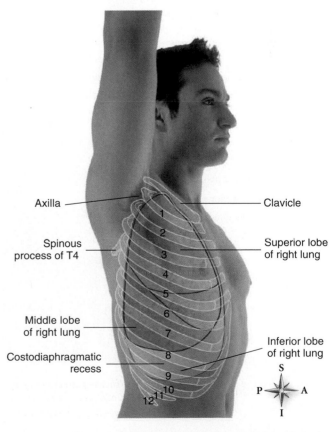

Figure 1-12 *Thorax (showing rib cage and lungs; anterior view).* (From Drake RL: *Gray's atlas of anatomy,* New York, 2008, Elsevier.)

Figure 1-13 *Thorax (showing rib cage and lungs; posterior view).* (From Drake RL: *Gray's atlas of anatomy,* New York, 2008, Elsevier.)

Figure 1-14 *Thorax (showing rib cage and lungs; right lateral view).* (From Drake RL: *Gray's atlas of anatomy,* New York, 2008, Elsevier.)

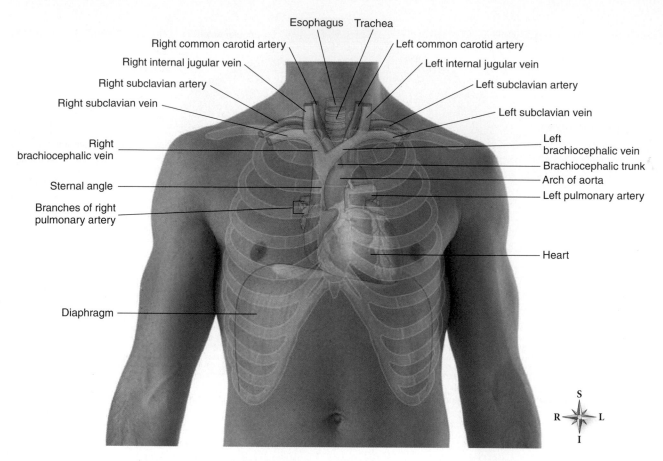

Figure 1-15 *Thorax (showing structures of the mediastinum; heart and large vessels).*
(From Drake RL: *Gray's atlas of anatomy,* New York, 2008, Elsevier.)

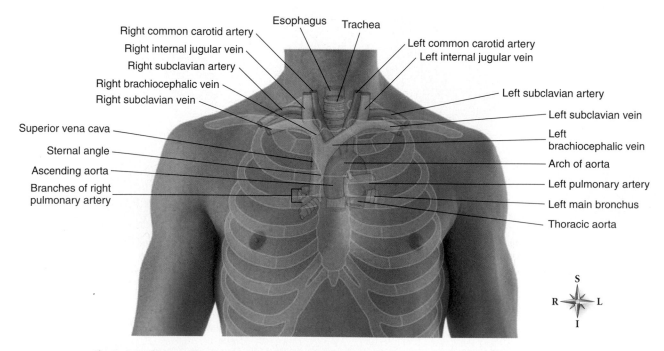

Figure 1-16 *Thorax (showing structures of the mediastinum; large vessels and airways [heart removed]).*
(From Drake RL: *Gray's atlas of anatomy,* New York, 2008, Elsevier.)

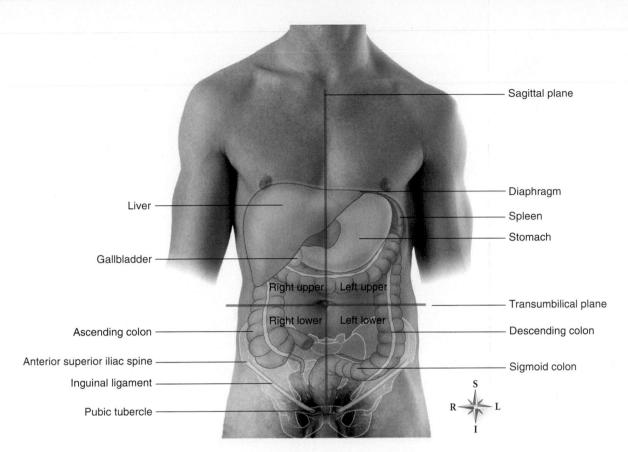

Sagittal plane

Diaphragm

Spleen

Stomach

Liver

Gallbladder

Right upper | Left upper

Transumbilical plane

Right lower | Left lower

Ascending colon

Descending colon

Anterior superior iliac spine

Sigmoid colon

Inguinal ligament

Pubic tubercle

S
R — L
I

Figure 1-17 *Abdominal quadrants and the positions of major organs.*
(From Drake RL: *Gray's atlas of anatomy,* New York, 2008, Elsevier.)

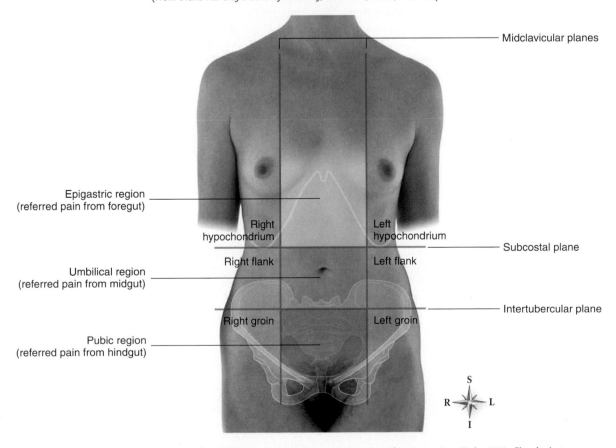

Midclavicular planes

Epigastric region
(referred pain from foregut)

Right
hypochondrium

Left
hypochondrium

Subcostal plane

Right flank

Left flank

Umbilical region
(referred pain from midgut)

Intertubercular plane

Right groin

Left groin

Pubic region
(referred pain from hindgut)

S
R — L
I

Figure 1-18 *Nine regions of the abdomen.* (From Drake RL: *Gray's atlas of anatomy,* New York, 2008, Elsevier.)

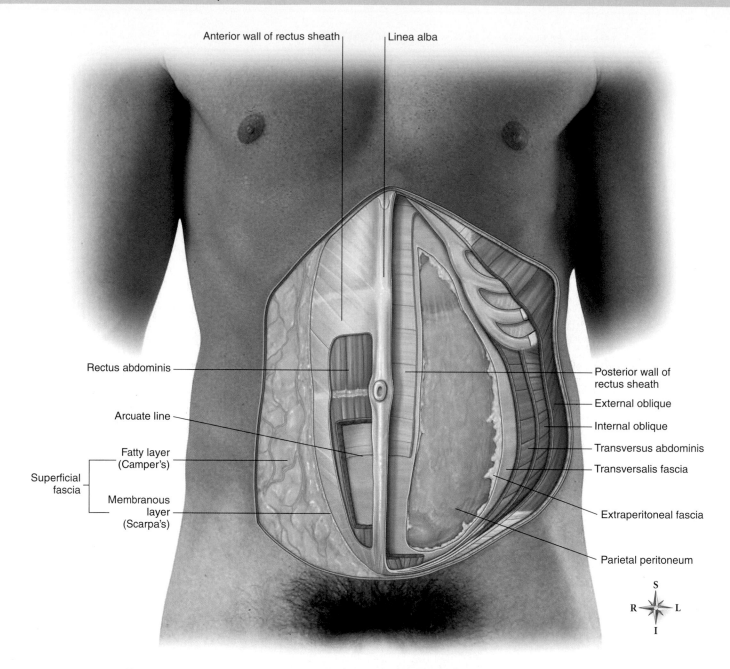

Figure 1-19 *Layers of the abdominal wall.* (From Drake RL: *Gray's atlas of anatomy,* New York, 2008, Elsevier.)

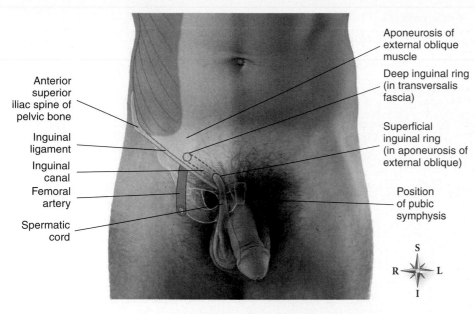

Anterior superior iliac spine of pelvic bone

Inguinal ligament

Inguinal canal

Femoral artery

Spermatic cord

Aponeurosis of external oblique muscle

Deep inguinal ring (in transversalis fascia)

Superficial inguinal ring (in aponeurosis of external oblique)

Position of pubic symphysis

Figure 1-20 *Inguinal region (male).* (From Drake RL: *Gray's atlas of anatomy*, New York, 2008, Elsevier.)

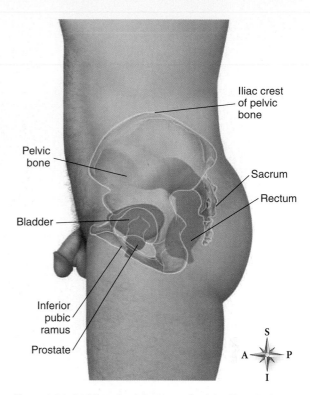

Iliac crest of pelvic bone

Pelvic bone

Sacrum

Rectum

Bladder

Inferior pubic ramus

Prostate

Figure 1-21 *Position of pelvic organs (male).* (From Drake RL: *Gray's atlas of anatomy*, New York, 2008, Elsevier.)

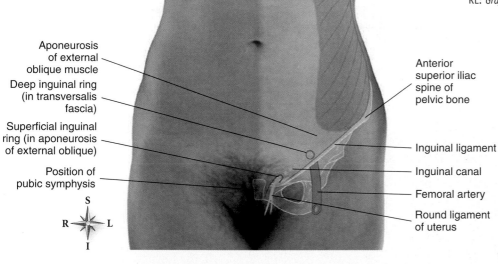

Aponeurosis of external oblique muscle

Deep inguinal ring (in transversalis fascia)

Superficial inguinal ring (in aponeurosis of external oblique)

Position of pubic symphysis

Anterior superior iliac spine of pelvic bone

Inguinal ligament

Inguinal canal

Femoral artery

Round ligament of uterus

Figure 1-22 *Inguinal region (female).* (From Drake RL: *Gray's atlas of anatomy*, New York, 2008, Elsevier.)

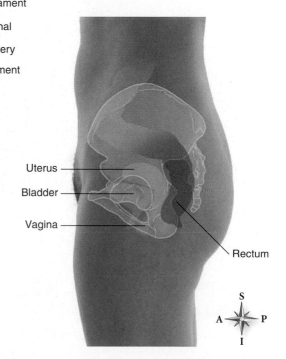

Uterus

Bladder

Vagina

Rectum

Figure 1-23 *Position of pelvic organs (female).* (From Drake RL: *Gray's atlas of anatomy*, New York, 2008, Elsevier.)

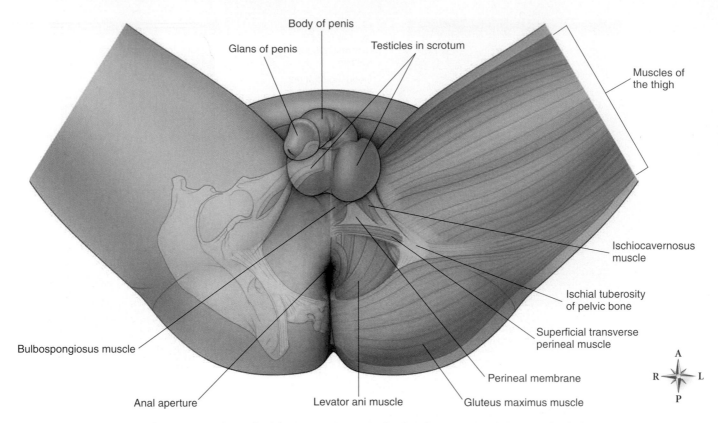

Body of penis

Glans of penis

Testicles in scrotum

Muscles of the thigh

Ischiocavernosus muscle

Ischial tuberosity of pelvic bone

Superficial transverse perineal muscle

Perineal membrane

Bulbospongiosus muscle

Anal aperture

Levator ani muscle

Gluteus maximus muscle

Figure 1-24 *Perineum (male).* (From Drake RL: *Gray's atlas of anatomy,* New York, 2008, Elsevier.)

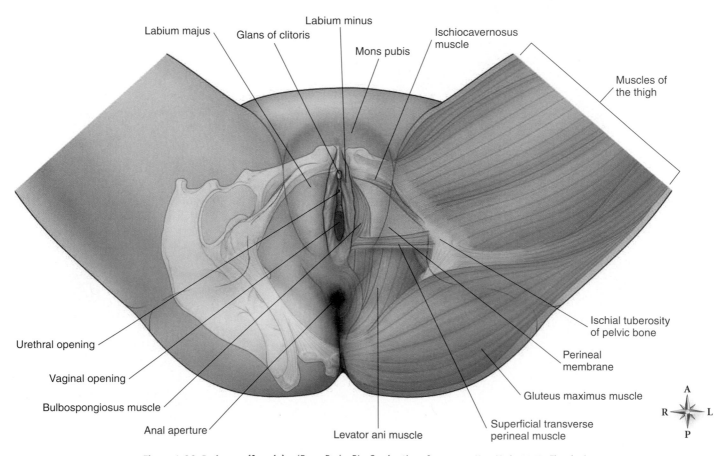

Labium majus

Glans of clitoris

Labium minus

Mons pubis

Ischiocavernosus muscle

Muscles of the thigh

Ischial tuberosity of pelvic bone

Perineal membrane

Urethral opening

Vaginal opening

Bulbospongiosus muscle

Anal aperture

Levator ani muscle

Superficial transverse perineal muscle

Gluteus maximus muscle

Figure 1-26 *Perineum (female).* (From Drake RL: *Gray's atlas of anatomy,* New York, 2008, Elsevier.)

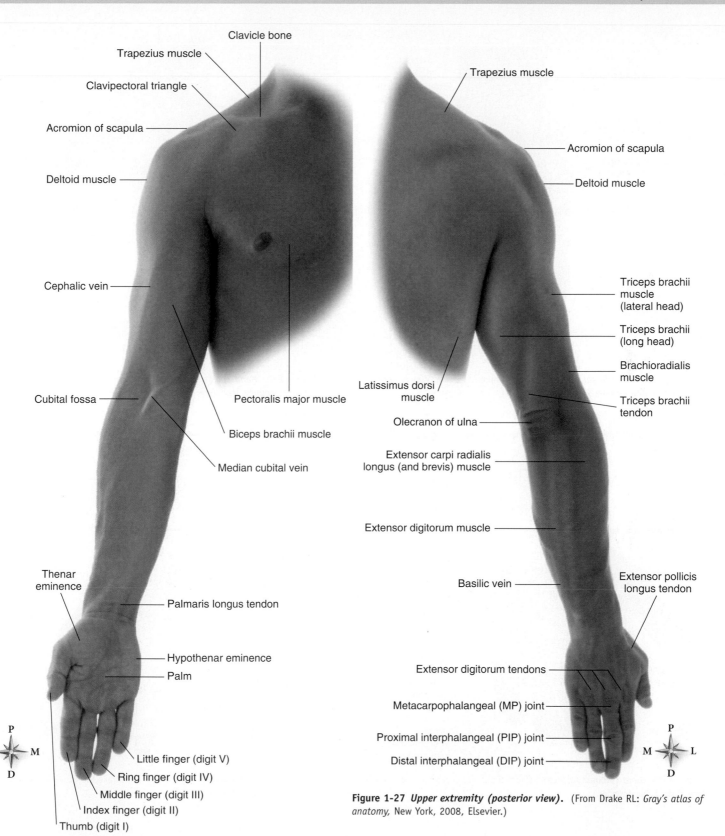

Clavicle bone

Trapezius muscle

Clavipectoral triangle

Acromion of scapula

Deltoid muscle

Cephalic vein

Cubital fossa

Pectoralis major muscle

Biceps brachii muscle

Median cubital vein

Thenar eminence

Palmaris longus tendon

Hypothenar eminence

Palm

Little finger (digit V)

Ring finger (digit IV)

Middle finger (digit III)

Index finger (digit II)

Thumb (digit I)

Trapezius muscle

Acromion of scapula

Deltoid muscle

Triceps brachii muscle (lateral head)

Triceps brachii (long head)

Brachioradialis muscle

Latissimus dorsi muscle

Triceps brachii tendon

Olecranon of ulna

Extensor carpi radialis longus (and brevis) muscle

Extensor digitorum muscle

Basilic vein

Extensor pollicis longus tendon

Extensor digitorum tendons

Metacarpophalangeal (MP) joint

Proximal interphalangeal (PIP) joint

Distal interphalangeal (DIP) joint

Figure 1-26 *Upper extremity (anterior view).* (From Drake RL: *Gray's atlas of anatomy,* New York, 2008, Elsevier.)

Figure 1-27 *Upper extremity (posterior view).* (From Drake RL: *Gray's atlas of anatomy,* New York, 2008, Elsevier.)

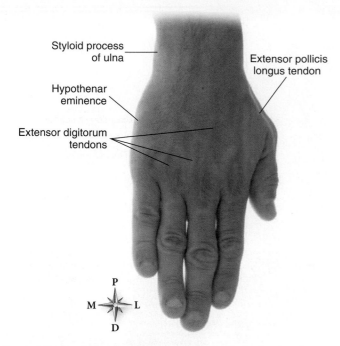

Styloid process of ulna

Hypothenar eminence

Extensor digitorum tendons

Extensor pollicis longus tendon

P
M — L
D

Figure 1-28 Hand (dorsal surface). (From Drake RL: *Gray's atlas of anatomy,* New York, 2008, Elsevier.)

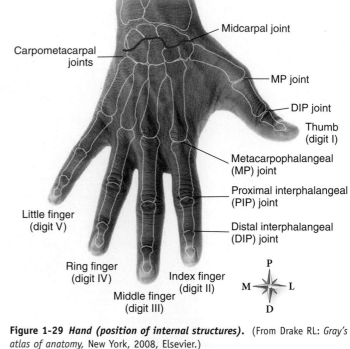

Midcarpal joint

Carpometacarpal joints

MP joint

DIP joint

Thumb (digit I)

Metacarpophalangeal (MP) joint

Proximal interphalangeal (PIP) joint

Distal interphalangeal (DIP) joint

Little finger (digit V)

Ring finger (digit IV)

Index finger (digit II)

Middle finger (digit III)

P
M — L
D

Figure 1-29 Hand (position of internal structures). (From Drake RL: *Gray's atlas of anatomy,* New York, 2008, Elsevier.)

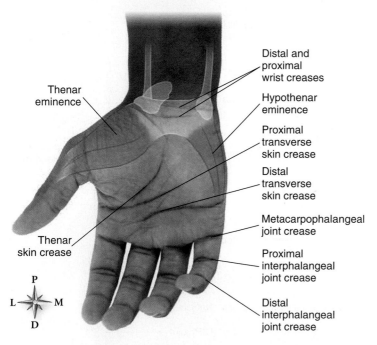

Thenar eminence

Distal and proximal wrist creases

Hypothenar eminence

Proximal transverse skin crease

Distal transverse skin crease

Metacarpophalangeal joint crease

Proximal interphalangeal joint crease

Thenar skin crease

Distal interphalangeal joint crease

L — M
P
D

Figure 1-30 Hand (palmar surface). (From Drake RL: *Gray's atlas of anatomy,* New York, 2008, Elsevier.)

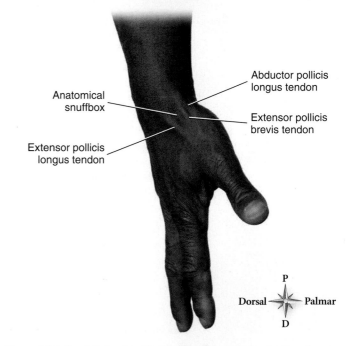

Abductor pollicis longus tendon

Anatomical snuffbox

Extensor pollicis brevis tendon

Extensor pollicis longus tendon

Dorsal — Palmar
P
D

Figure 1-31 Hand (lateral surface). (From Drake RL: *Gray's atlas of anatomy,* New York, 2008, Elsevier.)

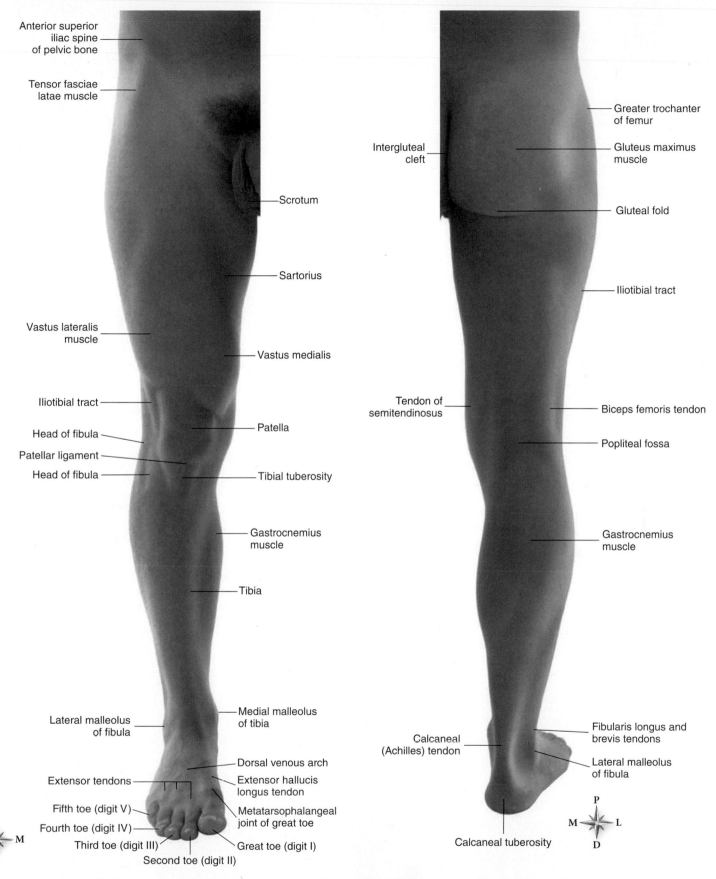

Anterior superior
iliac spine
of pelvic bone

Tensor fasciae
latae muscle

Scrotum

Sartorius

Vastus lateralis
muscle

Vastus medialis

Iliotibial tract

Patella

Head of fibula

Patellar ligament

Head of fibula

Tibial tuberosity

Gastrocnemius
muscle

Tibia

Lateral malleolus
of fibula

Medial malleolus
of tibia

Dorsal venous arch

Extensor tendons

Extensor hallucis
longus tendon

Fifth toe (digit V)

Fourth toe (digit IV)

Metatarsophalangeal
joint of great toe

Third toe (digit III)

Great toe (digit I)

Second toe (digit II)

Greater trochanter
of femur

Intergluteal
cleft

Gluteus maximus
muscle

Gluteal fold

Iliotibial tract

Tendon of
semitendinosus

Biceps femoris tendon

Popliteal fossa

Gastrocnemius
muscle

Calcaneal
(Achilles) tendon

Fibularis longus and
brevis tendons

Lateral malleolus
of fibula

Calcaneal tuberosity

Figure 1-32 *Lower extremity (anterior view).* (From Drake RL: *Gray's atlas of anatomy,* New York, 2008, Elsevier.)

Figure 1-33 *Lower extremity (posterior view).* (From Drake RL: *Gray's atlas of anatomy,* New York, 2008, Elsevier.)

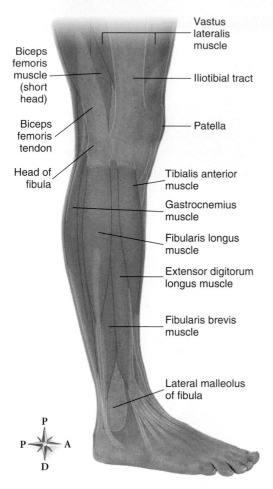

Vastus lateralis muscle

Biceps femoris muscle (short head)

Iliotibial tract

Biceps femoris tendon

Patella

Head of fibula

Tibialis anterior muscle

Gastrocnemius muscle

Fibularis longus muscle

Extensor digitorum longus muscle

Fibularis brevis muscle

Lateral malleolus of fibula

Figure 1-34 *Muscles of the leg (surface projection; right lateral view).* (From Drake RL: *Gray's atlas of anatomy,* New York, 2008, Elsevier.)

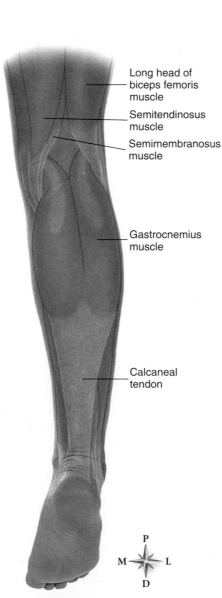

Long head of biceps femoris muscle

Semitendinosus muscle

Semimembranosus muscle

Gastrocnemius muscle

Calcaneal tendon

Figure 1-36 *Muscles of the leg (surface projection; posterior view).* (From Drake RL: *Gray's atlas of anatomy,* New York, 2008, Elsevier.)

Vastus lateralis muscle

Vastus medialis muscle

Quadriceps femoris tendon

Patella

Patellar ligament

Fibularis longus muscle

Tibialis anterior muscle

Gastrocnemius muscle

Tibia

Soleus muscle

Fibularis brevis muscle

Extensor digitorum longus muscle

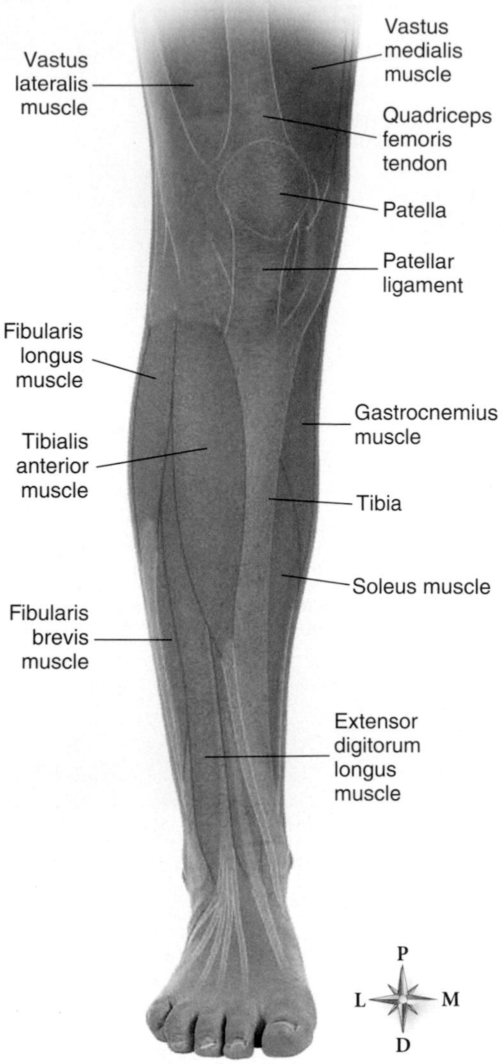

Figure 1-35 *Muscles of the leg (surface projection; anterior view).* (From Drake RL: *Gray's atlas of anatomy,* New York, 2008, Elsevier.)

PART 2

Skeleton

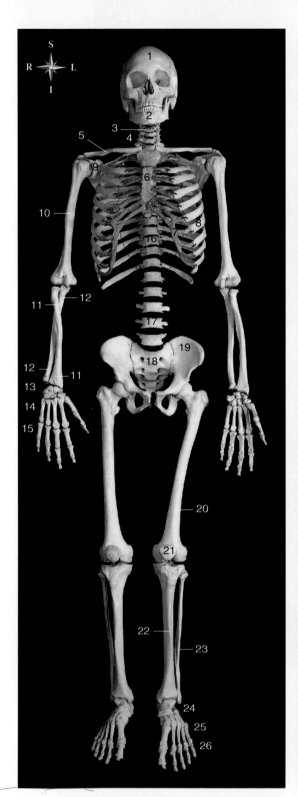

Figure 2-1 *Skeleton (anterior view).*

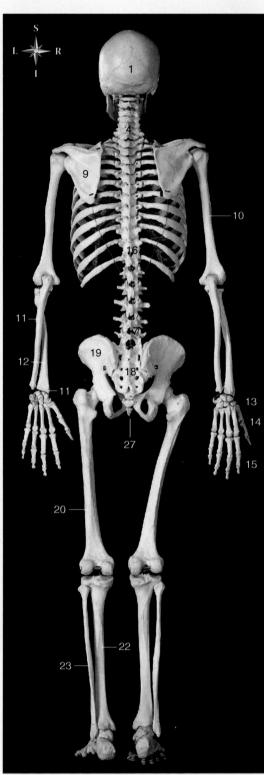

Figure 2-2 *Skeleton (posterior view).* The left forearm is supinated and the right forearm is pronated.

1 Skull
2 Mandible
3 Hyoid bone
4 Cervical vertebrae
5 Clavicle
6 Sternum
7 Costal cartilages
8 Ribs
9 Scapula
10 Humerus
11 Radius
12 Ulna
13 Carpal bones
14 Metacarpal bones
15 Phalanges of thumb
   and fingers
16 Thoracic vertebrae
17 Lumbar vertebrae
18 Sacrum
19 Hip bone
20 Femur
21 Patella
22 Tibia
23 Fibula
24 Tarsal bones
25 Metatarsal bones
26 Phalanges of toes
27 Coccyx

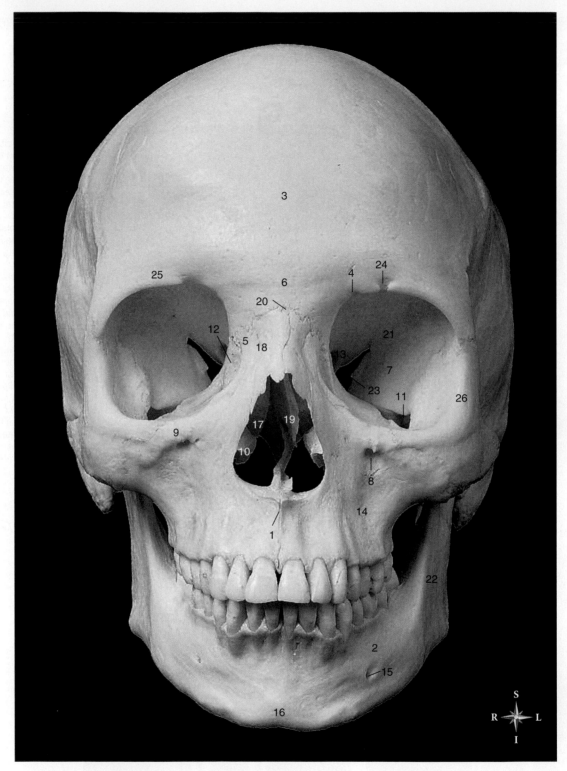

1 Anterior nasal spine
2 Body of mandible
3 Frontal bone
4 Frontal notch
5 Frontal process of maxilla
6 Glabella
7 Greater wing of sphenoid bone
8 Infraorbital foramen
9 Infraorbital margin
10 Inferior nasal concha
11 Inferior orbital fissure
12 Lacrimal bone
13 Lesser wing of sphenoid bone
14 Maxilla
15 Mental foramen
16 Mental protuberance
17 Middle nasal concha
18 Nasal bone
19 Nasal septum
20 Nasion
21 Orbit (orbital cavity)
22 Ramus of mandible
23 Superior orbital fissure
24 Supraorbital foramen
25 Supraorbital margin
26 Zygomatic bone

Figure 2-3 *Skull (frontal view).*

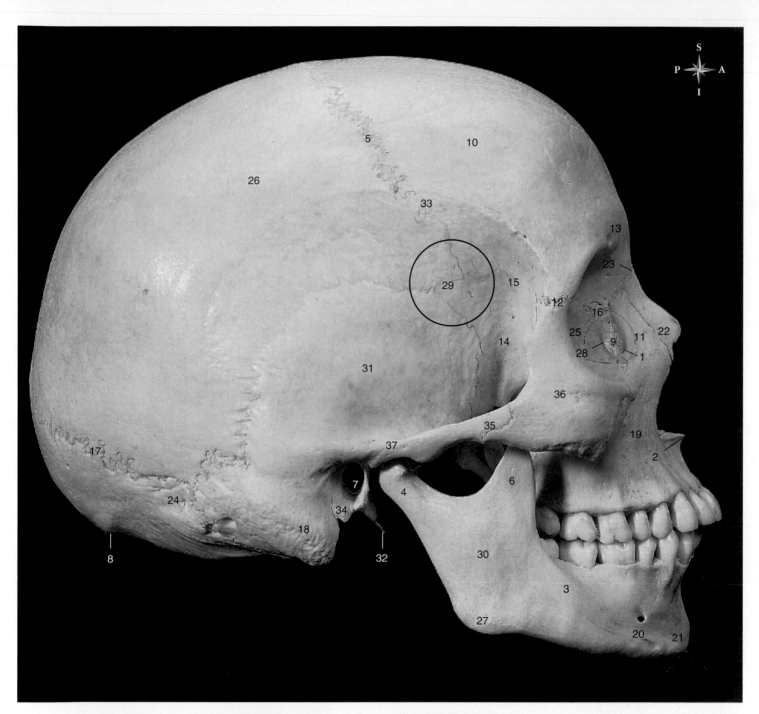

Figure 2-4 *Skull (right, lateral view).*

1 Anterior lacrimal crest
2 Anterior nasal spine
3 Body of mandible
4 Condyle of mandible
5 Coronal suture
6 Coronoid process of mandible
7 External acoustic meatus of temporal bone
8 External occipital protuberance (inion)
9 Fossa for lacrimal sac

10 Frontal bone
11 Frontal process of maxilla
12 Frontozygomatic suture
13 Glabella
14 Greater wing of sphenoid bone
15 Inferior temporal line
16 Lacrimal bone
17 Lambdoid suture
18 Mastoid process of temporal bone
19 Maxilla

20 Mental foramen
21 Mental protuberance
22 Nasal bone
23 Nasion
24 Occipital bone
25 Orbital part of ethmoid bone
26 Parietal bone
27 Angle of mandible
28 Posterior lacrimal crest
29 Pterion (encircled)
30 Ramus of mandible
31 Squamous part of temporal

bone
32 Styloid process of temporal bone
33 Superior temporal line
34 Tympanic part of temporal bone
35 Zygomatic arch
36 Zygomatic bone
37 Zygomatic process of temporal bone

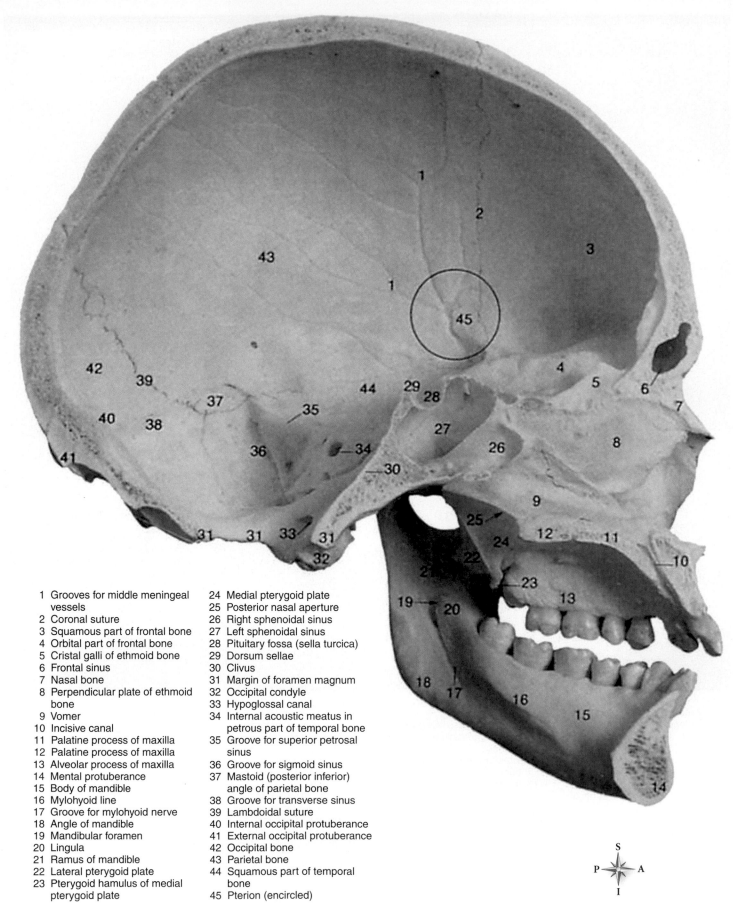

1 Grooves for middle meningeal
   vessels
2 Coronal suture
3 Squamous part of frontal bone
4 Orbital part of frontal bone
5 Cristal galli of ethmoid bone
6 Frontal sinus
7 Nasal bone
8 Perpendicular plate of ethmoid
   bone
9 Vomer
10 Incisive canal
11 Palatine process of maxilla
12 Palatine process of maxilla
13 Alveolar process of maxilla
14 Mental protuberance
15 Body of mandible
16 Mylohyoid line
17 Groove for mylohyoid nerve
18 Angle of mandible
19 Mandibular foramen
20 Lingula
21 Ramus of mandible
22 Lateral pterygoid plate
23 Pterygoid hamulus of medial
   pterygoid plate
24 Medial pterygoid plate
25 Posterior nasal aperture
26 Right sphenoidal sinus
27 Left sphenoidal sinus
28 Pituitary fossa (sella turcica)
29 Dorsum sellae
30 Clivus
31 Margin of foramen magnum
32 Occipital condyle
33 Hypoglossal canal
34 Internal acoustic meatus in
   petrous part of temporal bone
35 Groove for superior petrosal
   sinus
36 Groove for sigmoid sinus
37 Mastoid (posterior inferior)
   angle of parietal bone
38 Groove for transverse sinus
39 Lambdoidal suture
40 Internal occipital protuberance
41 External occipital protuberance
42 Occipital bone
43 Parietal bone
44 Squamous part of temporal
   bone
45 Pterion (encircled)

Figure 2-5 *Left half of the skull (sagittal section).*

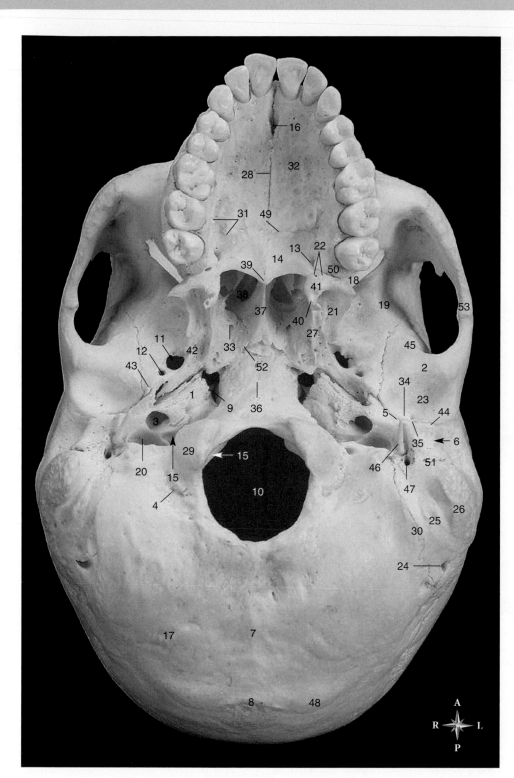

Figure 2-6 *Skull (external surface of the base).*

1 Apex of petrous part of temporal bone
2 Articular tubercle
3 Carotid canal
4 Condylar canal (posterior)
5 Edge of tegmen tympani
6 External acoustic meatus
7 External occipital crest
8 External occipital protuberance
9 Foramen lacerum
10 Foramen magnum
11 Foramen ovale
12 Foramen spinosum
13 Greater palatine foramen
14 Horizontal plate of palatine bone
15 Hypoglossal (anterior condylar) canal
16 Incisive fossa
17 Inferior nuchal line
18 Inferior orbital fissure
19 Infratemporal crest of greater wing of
     sphenoid bone
20 Jugular foramen
21 Lateral pterygoid plate
22 Lesser palatine foramina
23 Mandibular fossa
24 Mastoid foramen
25 Mastoid notch
26 Mastoid process
27 Medial pterygoid plate
28 Median palatine (intermaxillary) suture
29 Occipital condyle
30 Occipital groove
31 Palatine grooves and spines
32 Palatine process of maxilla
33 Palatinovaginal canal
34 Petrosquamous fissure
35 Petrotympanic fissure
36 Pharyngeal tubercle
37 Posterior border of vomer
38 Posterior nasal aperture (choana)
39 Posterior nasal spine
40 Pterygoid hamulus
41 Pyramidal process of palatine bone
42 Scaphoid fossa
43 Spine of sphenoid bone
44 Squamotympanic fissure
45 Squamous part of temporal bone
46 Styloid process
47 Stylomastoid foramen
48 Superior nuchal line
49 Transverse palatine (palatomaxillary) suture
50 Tuberosity of maxilla
51 Tympanic part of temporal bone
52 Vomerovaginal canal
53 Zygomatic arch

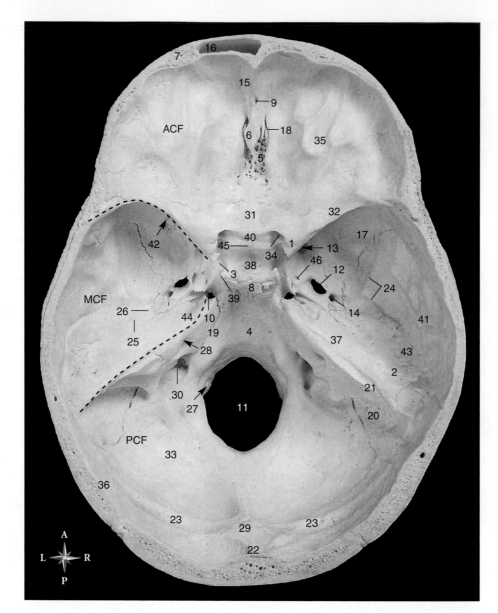

1 Anterior clinoid process
2 Arcuate eminence
3 Carotid groove
4 Clivus
5 Cribriform plate of
   ethmoid bone
6 Crista galli
7 Diploë
8 Dorsum sellae
9 Foramen cecum
10 Foramen lacerum
11 Foramen magnum
12 Foramen ovale
13 Foramen rotundum
14 Foramen spinosum
15 Frontal crest
16 Frontal sinus
17 Greater wing of
   sphenoid bone
18 Groove for anterior
   ethmoidal nerve and vessels
19 Groove for inferior
   petrosal sinus

20 Groove for sigmoid sinus
21 Groove for superior
   petrosal sinus
22 Groove for superior
   sagittal sinus
23 Groove for transverse
   sinus
24 Grooves for middle
   meningeal vessels
25 Hiatus and groove for
   greater petrosal nerve
26 Hiatus and groove for
   lesser petrosal nerve
27 Hypoglossal canal
28 Internal acoustic meatus
29 Internal occipital
   protuberance
30 Jugular foramen
31 Jugum of sphenoid bone
32 Lesser wing of
   sphenoid bone
33 Occipital bone
34 Optic canal

35 Orbital part of frontal bone
36 Parietal bone
   (posteroinferior angle only)
37 Petrous part of temporal
   bone
38 Pituitary fossa
   (sella turcica)
39 Posterior clinoid process
40 Prechiasmatic groove
41 Squamous part of
   temporal bone
42 Superior orbital fissure
43 Tegmen tympani
44 Trigeminal impression
45 Tuberculum sellae
46 Venous foramen

ACF, Anterior cranial fossa
MCF, Middle cranial fossa
PCF, Posterior cranial fossa

Figure 2-7 *Skull (internal surface of the base).*

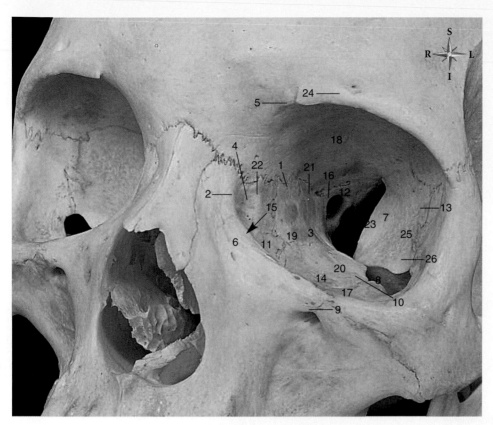

1 Anterior ethmoidal foramen
2 Anterior lacrimal crest
3 Body of sphenoid bone, forming medial wall
4 Fossa for lacrimal sac
5 Frontal notch
6 Frontal process of maxilla, forming medial wall
7 Greater wing of sphenoid bone, forming lateral wall
8 Inferior orbital fissure
9 Infraorbital foramen
10 Infraorbital groove
11 Lacrimal bone, forming medial wall
12 Lesser wing of sphenoid bone, forming roof
13 Marginal tubercle
14 Maxilla, forming floor
15 Nasolacrimal canal
16 Optic canal
17 Orbital border of zygomatic bone, forming floor
18 Orbital part of frontal bone, forming roof
19 Orbital plate of ethmoid bone, forming medial wall
20 Orbital process of palatine bone, forming floor
21 Posterior ethmoidal foramen
22 Posterior lacrimal crest
23 Superior orbital fissure
24 Supraorbital foramen
25 Zygomatic bone, forming lateral wall
26 Zygomatico-orbital foramen

Figure 2-8 *Skull (bones of the eye orbit)*.

1 Air cells of ethmoidal sinus
2 Clivus
3 Cribriform plate of ethmoid bone
4 Dorsum sellae
5 Ethmoidal bulla
6 Frontal sinus
7 Horizontal plate of palatine bone
8 Incisive canal
9 Inferior meatus
10 Inferior nasal concha
11 Lateral pterygoid plate
12 Left sphenoidal sinus
13 Medial pterygoid plate
14 Nasal bone
15 Nasal spine of frontal bone
16 Opening of maxillary sinus
17 Palatine process of maxilla
18 Perpendicular plate of palatine bone
19 Pituitary fossa (sella turcica)
20 Pterygoid hamulus
21 Right sphenoidal sinus
22 Semilunar hiatus
23 Sphenopalatine foramen
24 Uncinate process of ethmoid bone

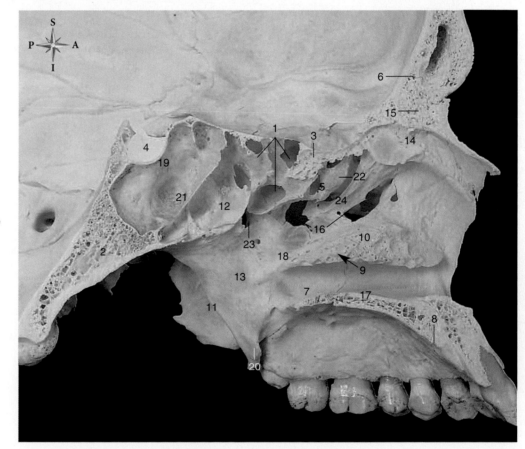

Figure 2-9 *Nasal cavity (lateral wall)*.

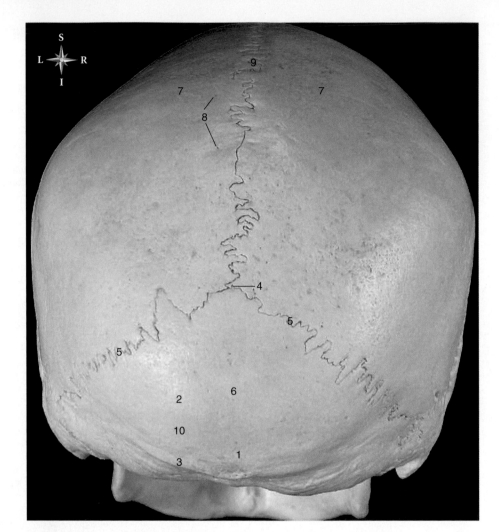

1 External occipital
   protuberance (inion)
2 Highest nuchal line
3 Inferior nuchal line
4 Lambda
5 Lambdoid suture
6 Occipital bone
7 Parietal bone
8 Parietal foramen
9 Sagittal suture
10 Superior nuchal line

Figure 2-10 *Skull (posterior view).*

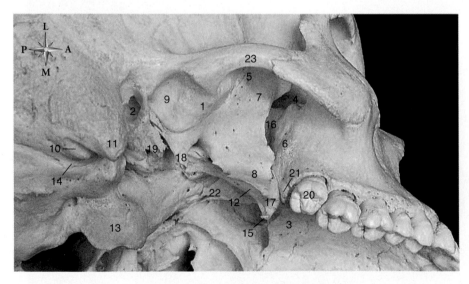

1 Articular tubercle
2 External acoustic
   meatus
3 Horizontal plate of
   palatine bone
4 Inferior orbital fissure
5 Infratemporal crest
6 Infratemporal
   (posterior) surface
   of maxilla
7 Infratemporal surface
   of greater wing of
   sphenoid bone
8 Lateral pterygoid plate
9 Mandibular fossa
10 Mastoid notch
11 Mastoid process

12 Medial pterygoid
   plate
13 Occipital condyle
14 Occipital groove
15 Pterygoid hamulus
16 Pterygomaxillary
   fissure and
   pterygopalatine fossa
17 Pyramidal process of
   palatine bone
18 Spine of sphenoid
   bone
19 Styloid process and
   sheath
20 Third molar tooth
21 Tuberosity of maxilla
22 Vomer
23 Zygomatic arch

Figure 2-11 *Skull (oblique inferior view).*

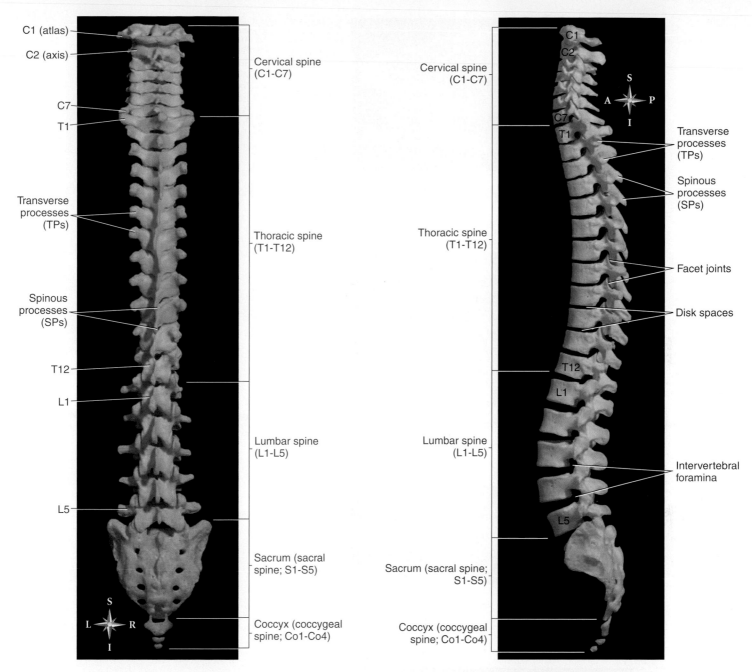

C1 (atlas)
C2 (axis)

C7
T1

Cervical spine
(C1-C7)

Transverse
processes
(TPs)

Thoracic spine
(T1-T12)

Spinous
processes
(SPs)

T12

L1

Lumbar spine
(L1-L5)

L5

S
L · R
I

Sacrum (sacral
spine; S1-S5)

Coccyx (coccygeal
spine; Co1-Co4)

Figure 2-12 *Vertebral column (posterior view).*

C1
C2

Cervical spine
(C1-C7)

C7
T1

S
A · P
I

Transverse
processes
(TPs)

Spinous
processes
(SPs)

Thoracic spine
(T1-T12)

Facet joints

Disk spaces

T12
L1

Lumbar spine
(L1-L5)

Intervertebral
foramina

L5

Sacrum (sacral spine;
S1-S5)

Coccyx (coccygeal
spine; Co1-Co4)

Figure 2-13 *Vertebral column (right lateral view).*

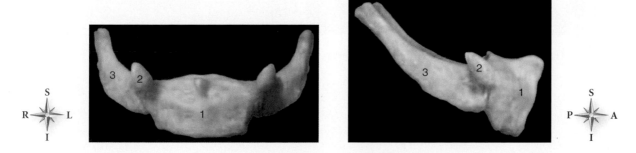

S
R · L
I

S
P · A
I

1 Body 2 Lesser cornu 3 Greater cornu

Figure 2-14 *Hyoid bone (anterior view [left]; right lateral view [right]).*

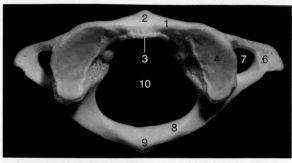

1 Anterior arch
2 Anterior tubercle
3 Facet for dens of axis (C2)
4 Superior articular process/facet
5 Inferior articular process/facet
6 Transverse process (TP)
7 Transverse foramen
8 Posterior arch
9 Posterior tubercle
10 Vertebral foramen
11 Lateral mass

Figure 2-15 *First cervical vertebra (superior view).*

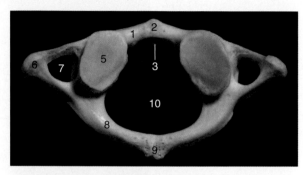

Figure 2-16 *First cervical vertebra (inferior view).*

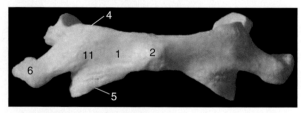

Figure 2-17 *First cervical vertebra (anterior view).*

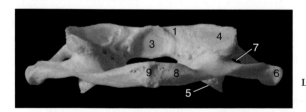

Figure 2-18 *First cervical vertebra (posterior view).*

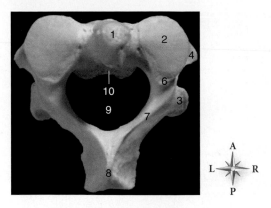
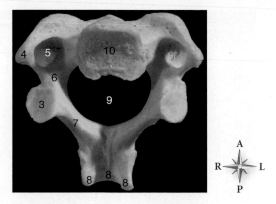

Figure 2-19 *Second cervical vertebra (C2; axis; superior view).*

Figure 2-20 *Second cervical vertebra (C2; axis; inferior view).*

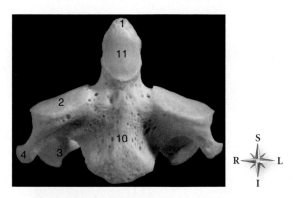
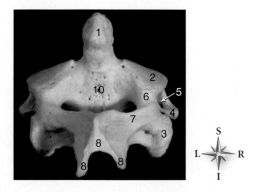

Figure 2-21 *Second cervical vertebra (C2; axis; anterior view).*

Figure 2-22 *Second cervical vertebra (C2; axis; posterior view).*

1 Dens (odontoid process)
2 Superior articular process/facet
3 Inferior articular process/facet
4 Transverse process (TP)
5 Transverse foramen
6 Pedicle
7 Lamina
8 Spinous process (SP) (bifid)
9 Vertebral foramen
10 Body
11 Facet on dens

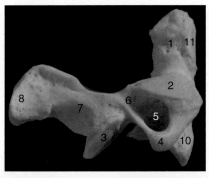

Figure 2-23 *Second cervical vertebra (C2; axis; right lateral view).*

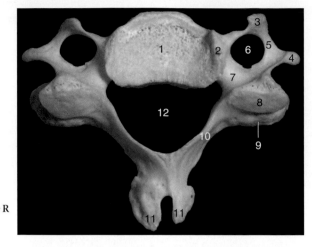

Figure 2-24 *Typical cervical vertebra (C5; superior view).*

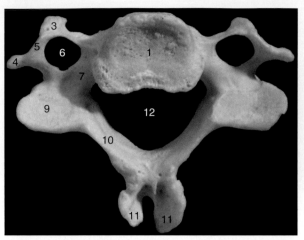

Figure 2-25 *Typical cervical vertebra (C5; inferior view).*

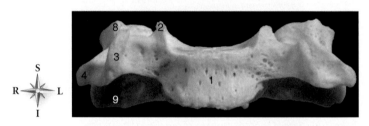

Figure 2-26 *Typical cervical vertebra (C5; anterior view).*

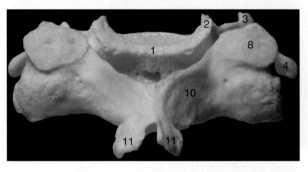

Figure 2-27 *Typical cervical vertebra (C5; posterior view).*

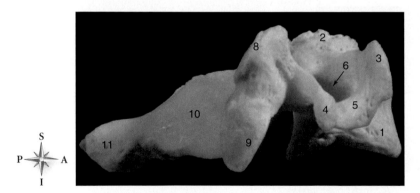

Figure 2-28 *Typical cervical vertebra (C5; right lateral view).*

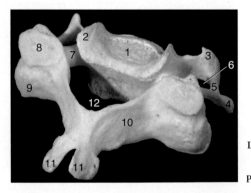

Figure 2-29 *Typical cervical vertebra (C5; oblique view [from above right]).*

1 Body
2 Uncus of body
3 Anterior tubercle of transverse process (TP)
4 Posterior tubercle of TP
5 Groove for spinal nerve (on TP)
6 Transverse foramen
7 Pedicle
8 Superior articular process/facet
9 Inferior articular process/facet
10 Lamina
11 Spinous process (SP) (bifid)
12 Vertebral foramen

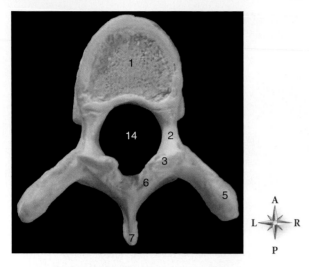

Figure 2-30 *Typical thoracic vertebra (T5; superior view).*

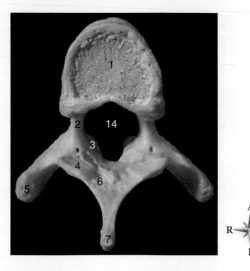

Figure 2-31 *Typical thoracic vertebra (T5; inferior view).*

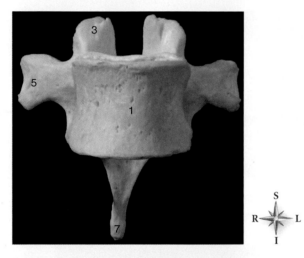

Figure 2-32 *Typical thoracic vertebra (T5; anterior view).*

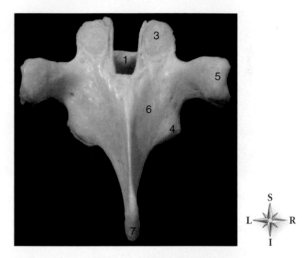

Figure 2-33 *Typical thoracic vertebra (T5; posterior view).*

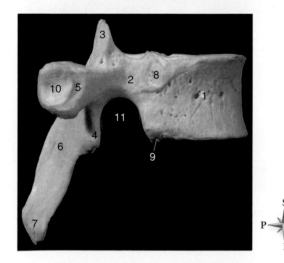

Figure 2-34 *Typical thoracic vertebra (T5; right lateral view).*

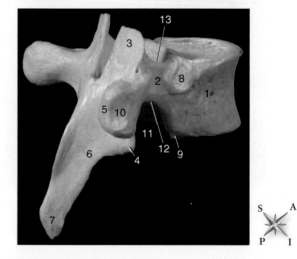

Figure 2-35 *Typical thoracic vertebra (T5; oblique view [from posterior right]).*

1 Body
2 Pedicle
3 Superior articular process/facet
4 Inferior articular process/facet
5 Transverse process (TP)
6 Lamina
7 Spinous process (SP)

8 Superior costal hemifacet
9 Inferior costal hemifacet
10 Transverse costal facet
11 Intervertebral foramen
12 Inferior vertebral notch
13 Superior vertebral notch
14 Vertebral foramen

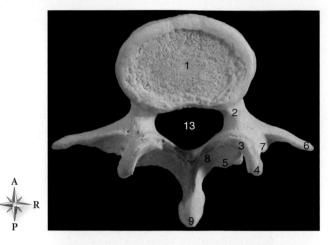

Figure 2-36 *Typical lumbar vertebra (L3; superior view).*

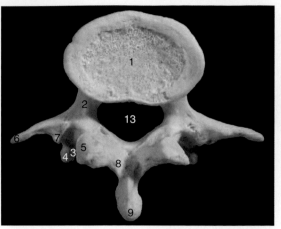

Figure 2-37 *Typical lumbar vertebra (L3; inferior view).*

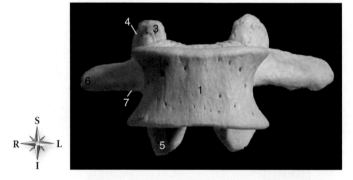

Figure 2-38 *Typical lumbar vertebra (L3; anterior view).*

Figure 2-39 *Typical lumbar vertebra (L3; posterior view).*

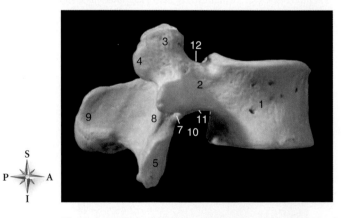

Figure 2-40 *Typical lumbar vertebra (L3; right lateral view).*

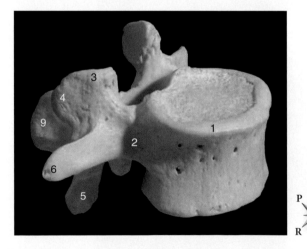

Figure 2-41 *Typical lumbar vertebra (L3; oblique view [from anterior right]).*

1 Body
2 Pedicle
3 Superior articular process/facet
4 Mamillary process
5 Inferior articular process/facet
6 Transverse process (TP)
7 Accessory process
8 Lamina
9 Spinous process (SP)
10 Intervertebral foramen
11 Inferior vertebral notch
12 Superior vertebral notch
13 Vertebral foramen

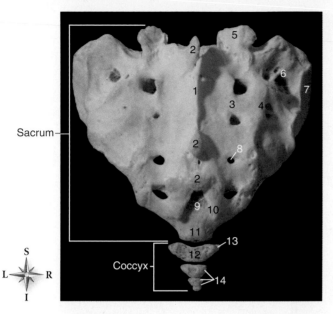

Figure 2-42 *Sacrum and coccyx (posterior view).*

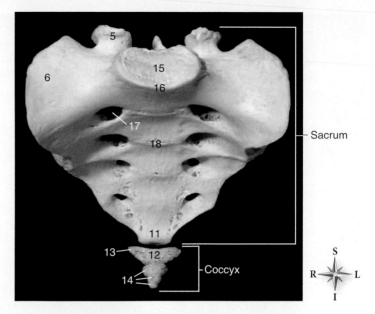

Figure 2-43 *Sacrum and coccyx (anterior view).*

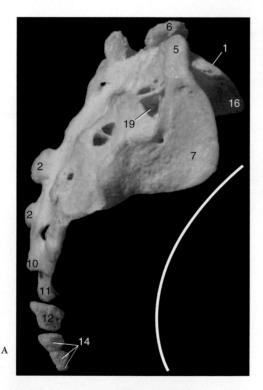

Figure 2-44 *Sacrum and coccyx (right lateral view).*

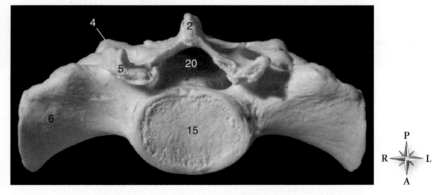

Figure 2-45 *Sacrum and coccyx (superior view).*

1 Median sacral crest
2 Tubercles along the median sacral crest
3 Intermediate sacral crest
4 Lateral sacral crest
5 Superior articular process/facet
6 Ala (wing)
7 Auricular surface (articular surface for ilium)
8 3rd Posterior foramen
9 Sacral hiatus
10 Sacral cornu
11 Apex
12 1st Coccygeal element
13 Coccygeal transverse process (TP)
14 2nd to 4th Coccygeal elements (fused)
15 Sacral base
16 Sacral promontory
17 1st Anterior foramen
18 Fusion of 2nd and 3rd sacral vertebrae
19 First posterior foramen
20 Sacral canal

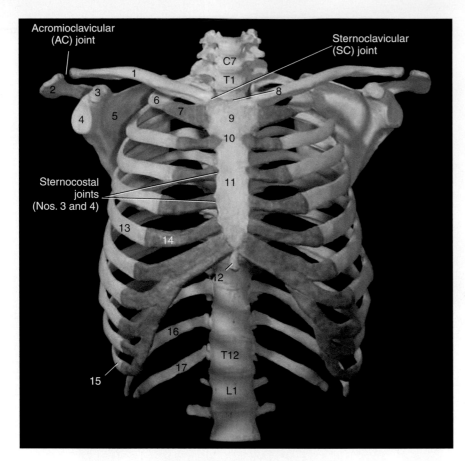

Figure 2-46 *Ribcage (anterior view).*

 1 Clavicle
 2 Acromion process
 3 Coracoid process
 4 Glenoid fossa
 5 Subscapular fossa
 6 1st rib
 7 Cartilage of 1st rib
 8 Sternal notch
 9 Manubrium of sternum
10 Sternal angle
11 Body of sternum
12 Xiphoid process of sternum
13 5th rib
14 Cartilage of 5th rib
15 10th rib
16 11th rib
17 12th rib
18 Clavicular notch of the manubrium
19 Notch for 1st costal cartilage
20 Notch for 2nd costal cartilage
21 Notch for 3rd costal cartilage
22 Notch for 4th costal cartilage
23 Notch for 5th costal cartilage
24 Notch for 6th costal cartilage
25 Notch for 7th costal cartilage

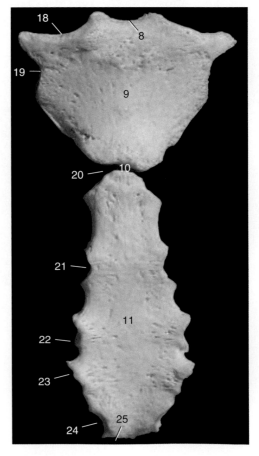

Figure 2-47 *Sterum.*

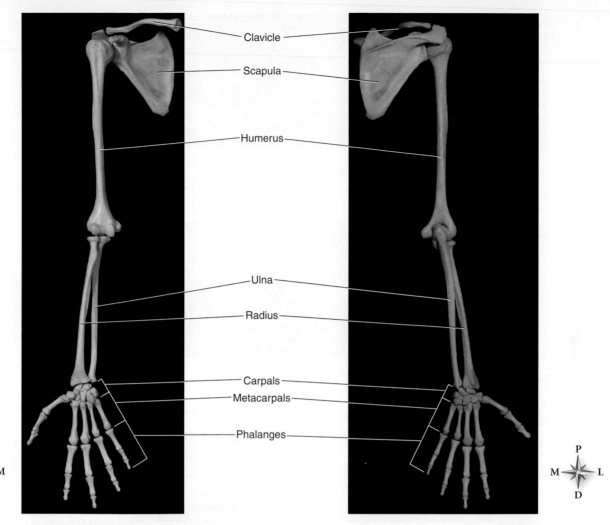

Figure 2-48 *Upper extremity (anterior view).*

Figure 2-49 *Upper extremity (posterior view).*

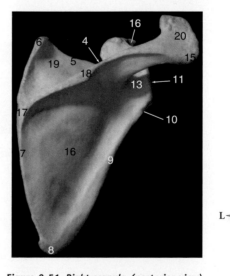

Figure 2-50 *Right scapula (anterior view).*

Figure 2-51 *Right scapula (posterior view).*

1 Acromion process	8 Inferior angle	15 Acromial organizer
2 Apex of coracoid process	9 Lateral border	16 Infraspinous fossa
3 Base of coracoid process	10 Infraglenoid tubercle	17 Root of the spine
4 Suprascapular notch	11 Glenoid fossa	18 Spine
5 Superior border	12 Supraglenoid tubercle	19 Supraspinous fossa
6 Superior angle	13 Neck	20 Coracoid process
7 Medial border	14 Subscapular fossa	

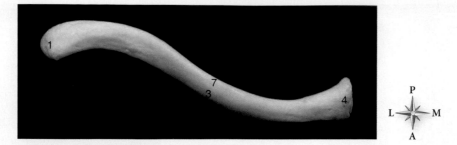

Figure 2-52 *Right clavicle (superior view)*.

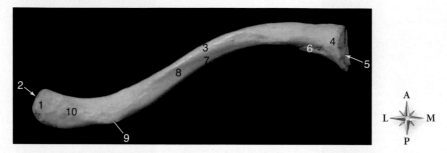

Figure 2-53 *Right clavicle (inferior view)*.

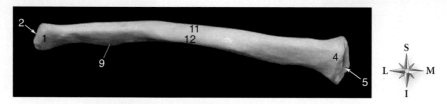

Figure 2-54 *Right clavicle (anterior view)*.

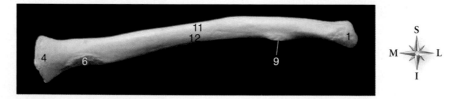

Figure 2-55 *Right clavicle (posterior view)*.

 1 Acromial end
 2 Articular surface for acromioclavicular (AC) joint
 3 Anterior border
 4 Sternal end
 5 Articular surface for sternoclavicular joint
 6 Costal tubercle
 7 Posterior border
 8 Subclavian groove
 9 Conoid tubercle
10 Trapezoid line
11 Superior border
12 Inferior border

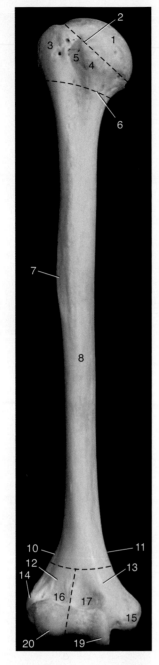

Figure 2-56 *Right humerus (anterior view).*

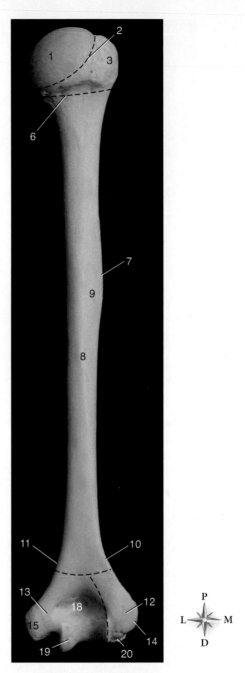

Figure 2-57 *Right humerus (posterior view).*

1 Head	11 Medial supracondylar ridge
2 Anatomic neck	12 Lateral condyle
3 Greater tubercle	13 Medial condyle
4 Lesser tubercle	14 Lateral epicondyle
5 Bicipital groove	15 Medial epicondyle
6 Surgical neck	16 Radial fossa
7 Deltoid tuberosity	17 Coronoid fossa
8 Body (shaft)	18 Olecranon fossa
9 Groove for radial nerve	19 Trochlea
10 Lateral supracondylar ridge	20 Capitulum

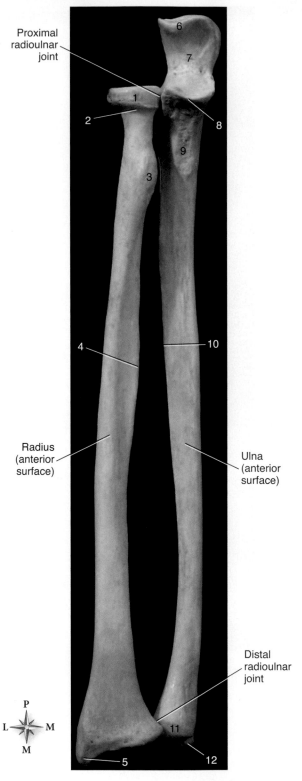

Proximal
radioulnar
joint

Radius
(anterior
surface)

Ulna
(anterior
surface)

Distal
radioulnar
joint

P
L ✦ M
M

Figure 2-58 *Right radius and ulna (anterior view).*

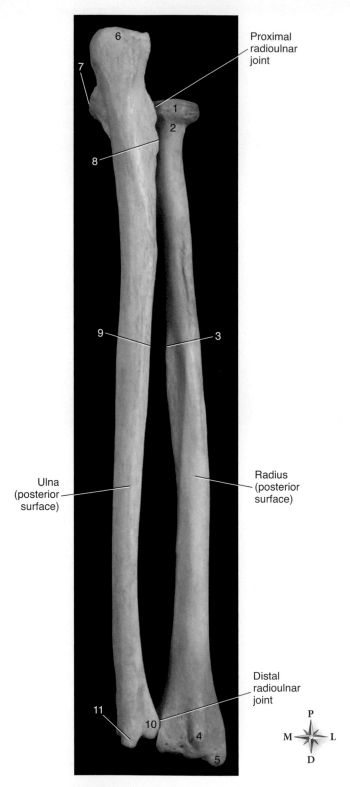

Proximal
radioulnar
joint

Ulna
(posterior
surface)

Radius
(posterior
surface)

Distal
radioulnar
joint

P
M ✦ L
D

Figure 2-59 *Right radius and ulna (posterior view).*

Landmarks of the Radius
1 Head
2 Neck
3 Tuberosity
4 Interosseus crest
5 Styloid process

Landmarks of the Ulna
6 Olecranon process
7 Trochlear notch
8 Coronoid process
9 Tuberosity
10 Interosseus crest
11 Head
12 Styloid process

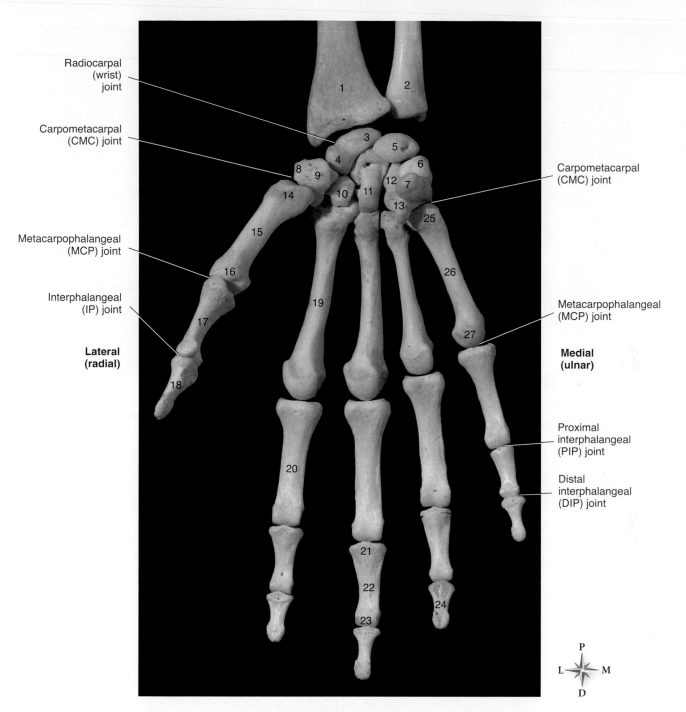

Figure 2-60 *Wrist and hand (anterior view).*

1 Radius
2 Ulna
3 Scaphoid
4 Tubercle of scaphoid
5 Lunate
6 Triquetrum
7 Pisiform
8 Trapezium
9 Tubercle of trapezium
10 Trapezoid
11 Capitate
12 Hamate
13 Hook of hamate
14 Base of 1st metacarpal (of thumb)

15 Body (shaft) of 1st metacarpal (of thumb)
16 Head of 1st metacarpal (of thumb)
17 Proximal phalanx of thumb
18 Distal phalanx of thumb
19 2nd Metacarpal (of index finger)
20 Proximal phalanx of index finger
21 Base of middle phalanx of middle finger
22 Body (shaft) of middle phalanx of middle finger
23 Head of middle phalanx of middle finger
24 Distal phalanx of ring finger
25 Base of 5th metacarpal (of little finger)
26 Body (shaft) of 5th metacarpal (of little finger)
27 Head of 5th metacarpal (of little finger)

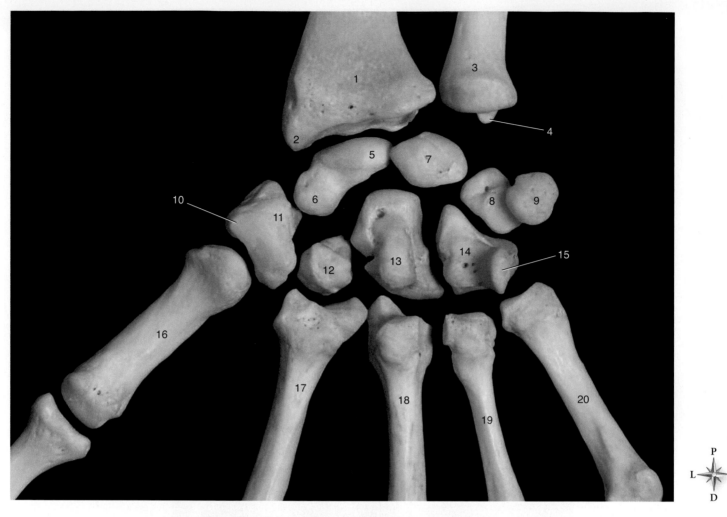

Figure 2-61 *Right carpal bones (separated; anterior view).*

1 Radius	11 Tubercle of trapezium
2 Styloid process of radius	12 Trapezoid
3 Ulna	13 Capitate
4 Styloid process of ulna	14 Hamate
5 Scaphoid	15 Hook of hamate
6 Tubercle of scaphoid	16 1st Metacarpal (of thumb)
7 Lunate	17 2nd Metacarpal (of index finger)
8 Triquetrum	18 3rd Metacarpal (of middle finger)
9 Pisiform	19 4th Metacarpal (of ring finger)
10 Trapezium	20 5th Metacarpal (of little finger)

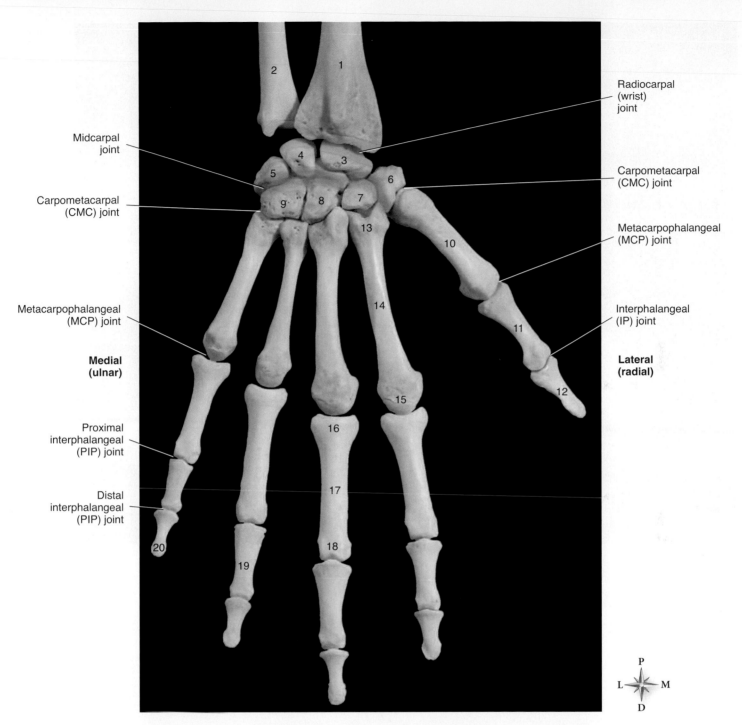

Figure 2-62 *Right wrist and hand (posterior view).*

1 Radius	11 Proximal phalanx of thumb
2 Ulna	12 Distal phalanx of thumb
3 Scaphoid	13 Base of metacarpal of index finger
4 Lunate	14 Body (shaft) of metacarpal of index finger
5 Triquetrum	15 Head of metacarpal of index finger
6 Trapezium	16 Base of proximal phalanx of middle finger
7 Trapezoid	17 Body (shaft) of proximal phalanx of middle finger
8 Capitate	18 Head of proximal phalanx of middle finger
9 Hamate	19 Middle phalanx of little finger
10 1st Metacarpal (of thumb)	20 Distal phalanx of little finger

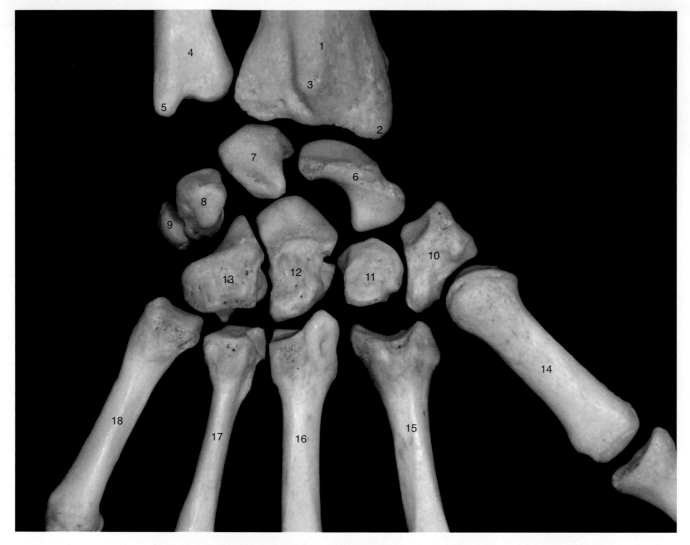

Figure 2-63 *Right carpal bones (separated; posterior view).*

1 Radius	10 Trapezium
2 Styloid process of radius	11 Trapezoid
3 Dorsal tubercle of radius	12 Capitate
4 Ulna	13 Hamate
5 Styloid process of ulna	14 1st Metacarpal (of thumb)
6 Scaphoid	15 2nd Metacarpal (of index finger)
7 Lunate	16 3rd Metacarpal (of middle finger
8 Triquetrum	17 4th Metacarpal (of ring finger)
9 Pisiform	18 5th Metacarpal (of little finger)

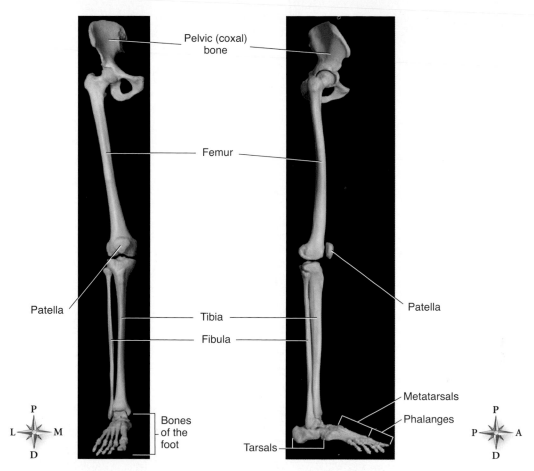

Figure 2-64 *Right lower extremity (anterior view).*   Figure 2-65 *Right lower extremity (posterior view).*

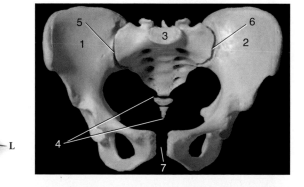

Figure 2-66 *Pelvis (anterior view).*

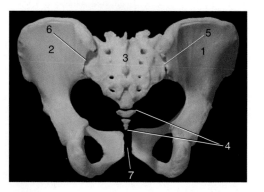

Figure 2-67 *Pelvis (posterior view).*

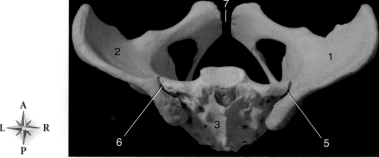

1 Right pelvic (coxal) bone
2 Left pelvic (coxal) bone
3 Sacrum
4 Coccyx
5 Right sacroiliac (SI) joint
6 Left SI joint
7 Pubic symphysis joint

Figure 2-68 *Pelvis (superior view).*

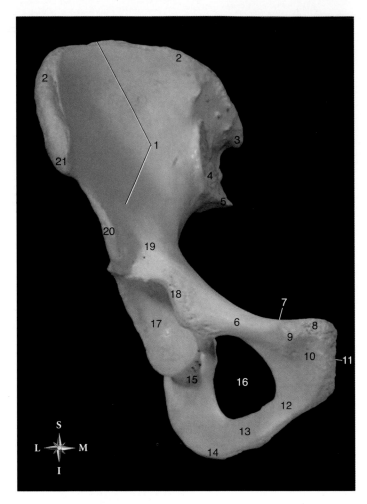

Figure 2-69 *Right pelvic bone (coxal; anterior view).*

1 Wing of the ilium (iliac fossa on internal surface)
2 Iliac crest
3 Posterior superior iliac spine (PSIS)
4 Articular surface for sacroiliac joint
5 Posterior inferior iliac spine (PIIS)
6 Superior ramus of pubis
7 Pectineal line of pubis
8 Pubic crest
9 Pubic tubercle
10 Body of pubis
11 Articular surface for pubic symphysis
12 Inferior ramus of pubis
13 Ramus of ischium
14 Ischial tuberosity
15 Body of ischium
16 Obturator foramen
17 Acetabulum
18 Rim of acetabulum
19 Body of ilium
20 Anterior inferior iliac spine (AIIS)
21 Anterior superior iliac spine (ASIS)

1 Wing of the ilium (iliac fossa on internal surface)
2 Iliac crest
3 Anterior superior iliac spine (ASIS)
4 Rim of acetabulum
5 Ischial spine
6 Body of ischium
7 Ischial tuberosity
8 Ramus of ischium
9 Inferior ramus of pubis
10 Body of pubis
11 Superior ramus of pubis
12 Pectineal line of pubis
13 Obturator foramen
14 Body of ilium
15 Posterior inferior iliac spine (PIIS)
16 Posterior superior iliac spine (PSIS)
17 Inferior gluteal line *(dashed line)*
18 Anterior gluteal line *(dashed line)*
19 Posterior gluteal line *(dashed line)*
20 Greater sciatic notch
21 Lesser sciatic notch

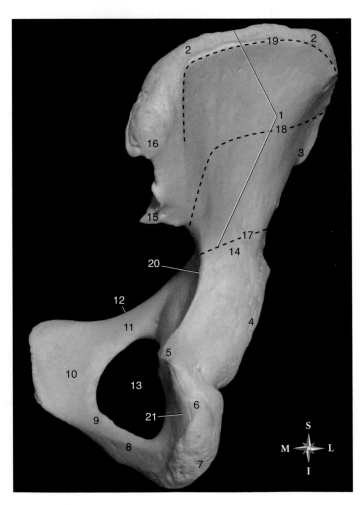

Figure 2-70 *Right pelvic bone (coxal; posterior view).*

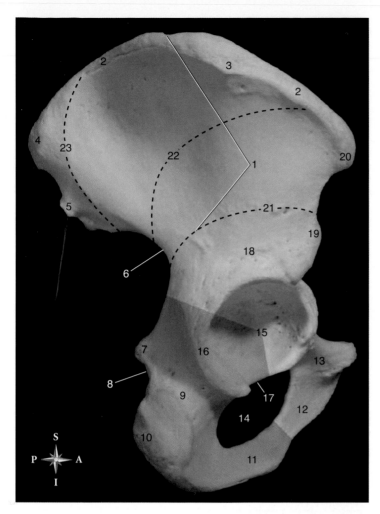

Figure 2-71 *Right pelvic bone (coxal; lateral view).* *Blue,* Ilium; *pink,* ischium; *yellow,* pubis.

1 Wing of the ilium (iliac fossa on internal surface)
2 Iliac crest
3 Anterior superior iliac spine (ASIS)
4 Rim of acetabulum
5 Ischial spine
6 Body of ischium
7 Ischial tuberosity
8 Ramus of ischium
9 Inferior ramus of pubis
10 Body of pubis
11 Superior ramus of pubis
12 Pectineal line of pubis
13 Obturator foramen
14 Body of ilium
15 Posterior inferior iliac spine (PIIS)
16 Posterior superior iliac spine (PSIS)
17 Inferior gluteal line *(dashed line)*
18 Anterior gluteal line *(dashed line)*
19 Posterior gluteal line *(dashed line)*
20 Greater sciatic notch
21 Lesser sciatic notch

1 Wing of the ilium (iliac fossa on
   internal surface)
2 Iliac crest
3 Posterior superior iliac spine (PSIS)
4 Iliac tuberosity
5 Articular surface of ilium for sacroiliac joint
6 Posterior inferior iliac spine (PIIS)
7 Greater sciatic notch
8 Ischial spine
9 Lesser sciatic notch
10 Body of ischium
11 Ischial tuberosity
12 Ramus of ischium
13 Inferior ramus of pubis
14 Articular surface of pubis for pubis symphysis
15 Pubic tubercle
16 Superior ramus of pubis
17 Pectineal line of pubis
18 Body of pubis
19 Iliopectineal line
20 Arcuate line of the ilium
21 Obturator foramen
22 Body of ilium
23 Anterior inferior iliac spine (AIIS)
24 Anterior superior iliac spine (ASIS)

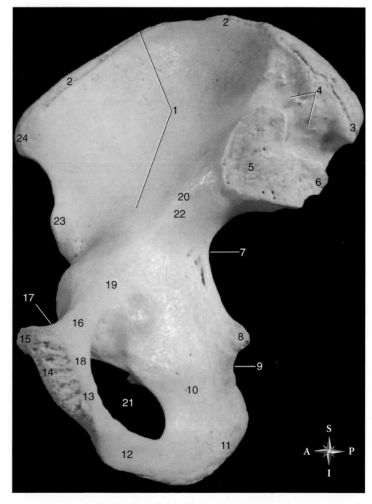

Figure 2-72 *Right pelvic bone (coxal; medial view).*

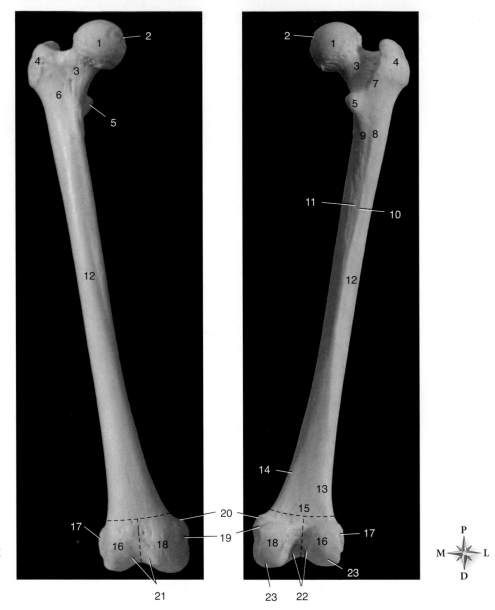

Figure 2-73 *Right femur (anterior view).*   **Figure 2-74** *Right femur (posterior view).*

1 Head	13 Lateral supracondylar line
2 Fovea of the head	14 Medial supracondylar line
3 Neck	15 Popliteal surface
4 Greater trochanter	16 Lateral condyle
5 Lesser trochanter	17 Lateral epicondyle
6 Intertrochanteric line	18 Medial condyle
7 Intertrochanteric crest	19 Medial epicondyle
8 Gluteal tuberosity	20 Adductor tubercle
9 Pectineal line	21 Articular surface for patellofemoral joint
10 Lateral lip of linea aspera	22 Intercondylar fossa
11 Medial lip of linea aspera	23 Articular surface for knee (tibiofemoral) joint
12 Body (shaft)	

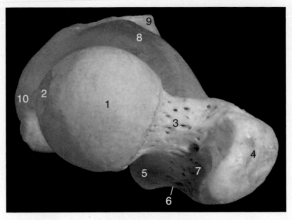

Figure 2-76 *Femur (proximal [superior] view).*

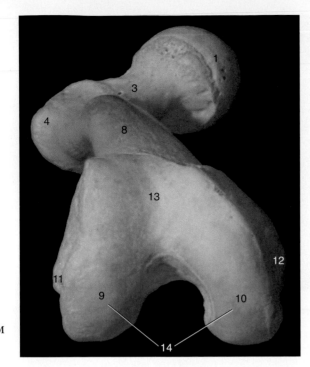

Figure 2-75 *Femur (distal [inferior] view).*

1 Head
2 Fovea of the head
3 Neck
4 Greater trochanter
5 Lesser trochanter
6 Intertrochanteric crest
7 Trochanteric fossa
8 Body (shaft), anterior surface
9 Lateral condyle
10 Medial condyle
11 Lateral epicondyle
12 Medial epicondyle
13 Articular surface for patellofemoral joint
14 Articular surface for knee (tibiofemoral) joint

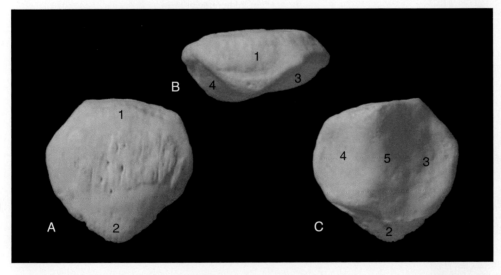

Figure 2-77 *Right patella (A, anterior view; B, proximal [superior] view; C, posterior view).*

1 Base
2 Apex
3 Facet for lateral condyle of femur
4 Facet for medial condyle of femur
5 Vertical ridge

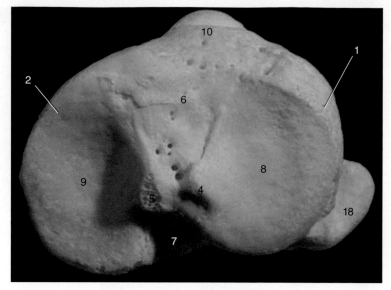

Figure 2-79 *Right tibia and fibula (proximal view).*

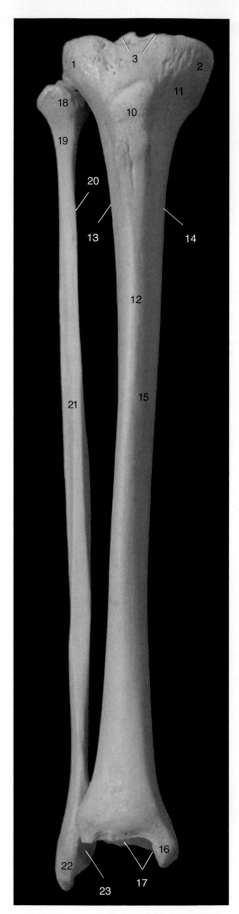

Figure 2-78 *Right tibia and fibula (anterior view).*

Tibial Landmarks:
1 Lateral condyle
2 Medial condyle
3 Intercondylar eminence
4 Lateral tubercle of intercondylar eminence
5 Medial tubercle of intercondylar eminence
6 Anterior intercondylar area
7 Posterior intercondylar area
8 Lateral facet (articular surface for knee [i.e., tibiofemoral] joint)
9 Medial facet (articular surface for knee [i.e., tibiofemoral] joint)
10 Tuberosity
11 Impression for iliotibial tract
12 Crest (i.e., anterior border)
13 Interosseus border
14 Medial border
15 Body (shaft)
16 Medial malleolus
17 Articular surface for ankle joint

Fibular Landmarks:
18 Head
19 Neck
20 Interosseus border
21 Body (shaft)
22 Lateral malleolus
23 Articular surface for ankle joint

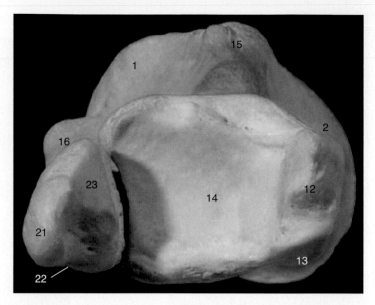

Figure 2-81 *Right tibia and fibula (distal view).*

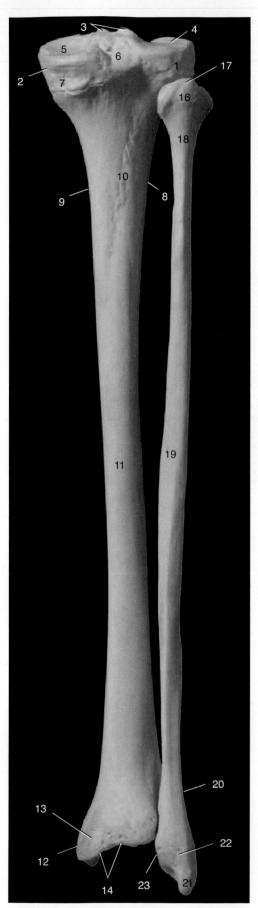

Figure 2-80 *Right tibia and fibula (posterior view).*

Tibial Landmarks:
 1 Lateral condyle
 2 Medial condyle
 3 Intercondylar eminence
 4 Lateral facet (articular surface for knee [i.e., tibiofemoral] joint)
 5 Medial facet (articular surface for knee [i.e., tibiofemoral] joint)
 6 Posterior intercondylar area
 7 Groove for semimembranosus muscle
 8 Interosseus border
 9 Medial border
10 Soleal line
11 Body (shaft)
12 Medial malleolus
13 Groove for tibialis posterior
14 Articular surfaces for ankle joint
15 Tuberosity

Fibular Landmarks:
16 Head
17 Apex of head
18 Neck
19 Body (shaft)
20 Lateral surface
21 Lateral malleolus
22 Groove for fibularis brevis
23 Articular surface for ankle joint

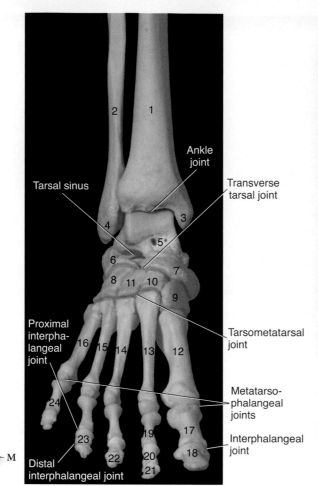

Figure 2-82 *Right ankle (anterior view).*

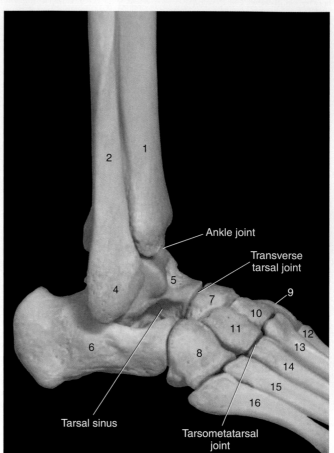

Figure 2-83 *Right ankle (lateral view).*

1 Tibia	13 2nd Metatarsal
2 Fibula	14 3rd Metatarsal
3 Medial malleolus (of tibia)	15 4th Metatarsal
4 Lateral malleolus (of fibula)	16 5th Metatarsal
5 Talus	17 Proximal phalanx of big toe
6 Calcaneus	18 Distal phalanx of big toe
7 Navicular	19 Proximal phalanx of 2nd toe
8 Cuboid	20 Middle phalanx of 2nd toe
9 1st Cuneiform	21 Distal phalanx of 2nd toe
10 2nd Cuneiform	22 Distal phalanx of 3rd toe
11 3rd Cuneiform	23 Middle phalanx of 4th toe
12 1st Metatarsal	24 Proximal phalanx of little toe (i.e., 5th toe)

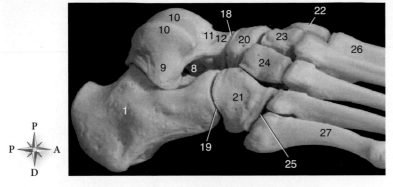

Figure 2-84 *Right ankle (subtalar joint; right lateral view).*

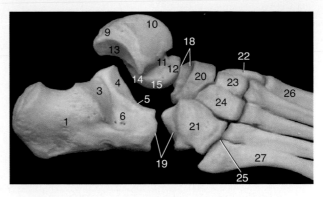

Figure 2-85 *Right ankle (subtalar joint; right lateral view; subtalar joint open).*

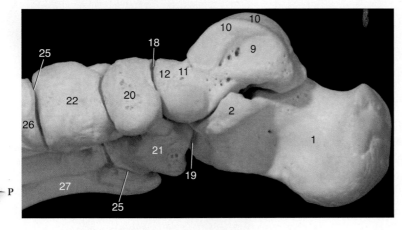

Figure 2-86 *Right ankle (subtalar joint; medial view).*

1 Calcaneus (#1-7)
2 Sustentaculum tali
3 Calcaneal posterior facet (of subtalar joint)
4 Calcaneal middle facet (of subtalar joint)
5 Calcaneal anterior facet (of subtalar joint)
6 Sulcus (of calcaneus)
7 Articular surface for calcaneocuboid joint (of transverse tarsal joint)
8 Tarsal sinus
9 Talus (#9-17)
10 Articular surface for ankle joint
11 Neck of talus
12 Head of talus
13 Talar posterior facet (of subtalar joint)
14 Talar middle facet (of subtalar joint)
15 Talar anterior facet (of subtalar joint)
16 Sulcus (of talus)
17 Articular surface for talonavicular joint (of transverse tarsal joint)
18 Talonavicular joint (of transverse tarsal joint)
19 Calcaneocuboid joint (of transverse tarsal joint)
20 Navicular
21 Cuboid
22 1st Cuneiform
23 2nd Cuneiform
24 3rd Cuneiform
25 Tarsometatarsal joint
26 1st Metatarsal
27 5th Metatarsal

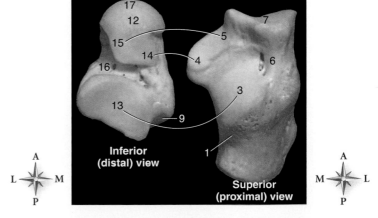

Figure 2-87 *Right ankle (subtalar joint; articular surfaces).*

1 Calcaneus
2 Fibular trochlea of calcaneus
3 Articular surface of talus for ankle joint
4 Medial tubercle of talus
5 Lateral tubercle of talus
6 Neck of talus
7 Head of talus
8 Navicular
9 Navicular tuberosity
10 Cuboid
11 Groove for fibularis longus
12 1st Cuneiform
13 2nd Cuneiform
14 3rd Cuneiform
15 Base of 1st metatarsal
16 Body (shaft) of 1st metatarsal
17 Head of 1st metatarsal
18 Tuberosity of base of 5th metatarsal
19 Base of 5th metatarsal
20 Body (shaft) of 5th metatarsal
21 Head of 5th metatarsal
22 Sesamoid bone of big toe
23 Proximal phalanx of big toe
24 Distal phalanx of big toe
25 Base of proximal phalanx of 2nd toe
26 Body (shaft) of proximal phalanx of 2nd toe
27 Head of proximal phalanx of 2nd toe
28 Middle phalanx of 3rd toe
29 Distal phalanx of 4th toe

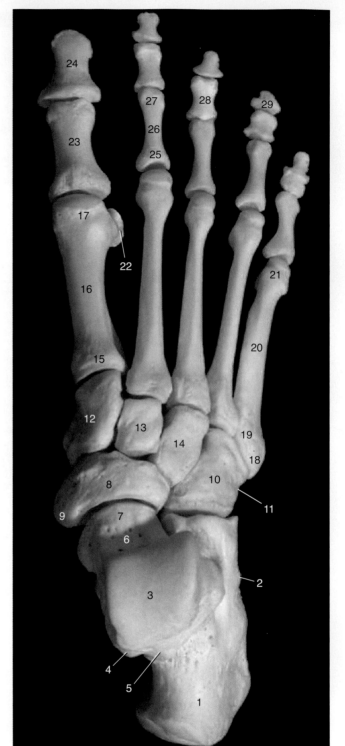

Figure 2-88 *Right foot (dorsal view).*

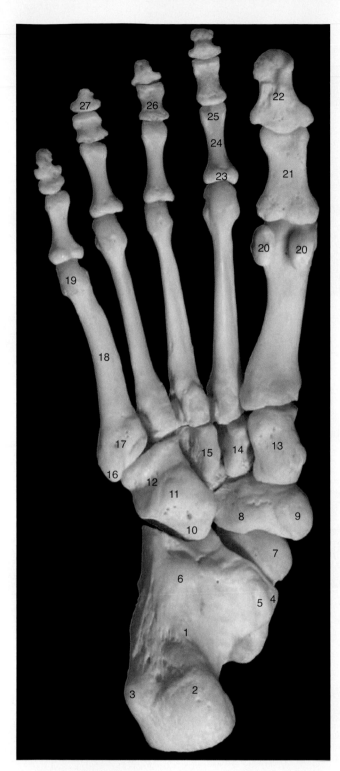

Figure 2-89 *Right foot (plantar view).*

1 Calcaneus
2 Medial process of calcaneal tuberosity
3 Lateral process of calcaneal tuberosity
4 Sustentaculum tali of calcaneus
5 Groove for distal tendon of flexor hallucis longus muscle
   (on sustentaculum tali)
6 Anterior tubercle of calcaneus
7 Head of talus
8 Navicular
9 Navicular tuberosity
10 Cuboid
11 Tuberosity of cuboid
12 Groove for distal tendon of fibularis longus muscle
13 1st Cuneiform
14 2nd Cuneiform
15 3rd Cuneiform
16 Tuberosity of base of 5th metatarsal
17 Base of 5th metatarsal
18 Body (shaft) of 5th metatarsal
19 Head of 5th metatarsal
20 Sesamoid bone of big toe
21 Proximal phalanx of big toe
22 Distal phalanx of big toe
23 Base of proximal phalanx of 2nd toe
24 Body (shaft) of proximal phalanx of 2nd toe
25 Head of proximal phalanx of 2nd toe
26 Middle phalanx of 3rd toe
27 Distal phalanx of 4th toe

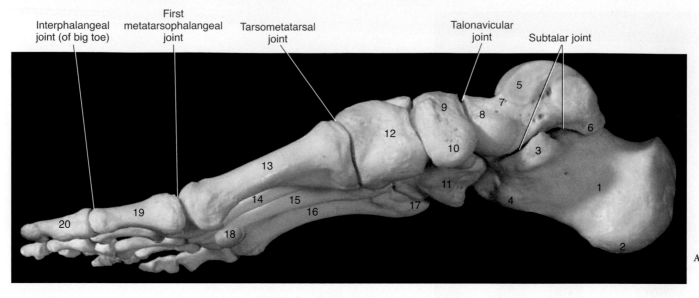

Figure 2-90 *Right foot (medial view).*

1 Calcaneus (medial surface)	7 Neck of talus	15 4th Metatarsal
2 Medial process of calcaneal tuberosity	8 Head of talus	16 5th Metatarsal
3 Sustentaculum tali of calcaneus	9 Navicular	17 Tuberosity of base of 5th metatarsal
4 Anterior tubercle of calcaneus	10 Navicular tuberosity	18 Sesamoid bone of big toe
5 Articular surface of talus for (medial malleolus of) ankle joint	11 Cuboid	19 Proximal phalanx of big toe
6 Medial tubercle of talus	12 1st Cuneiform	20 Distal phalanx of big toe
	13 1st Metatarsal	
	14 3rd Metatarsal	

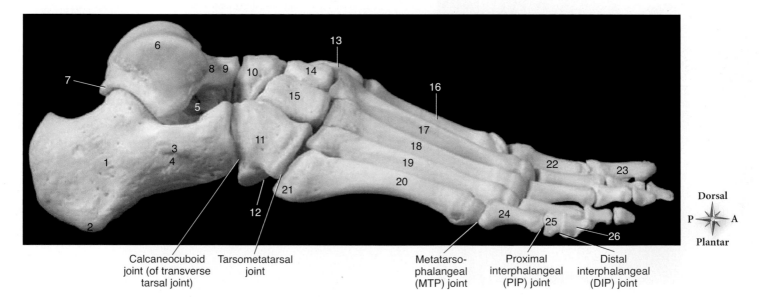

Figure 2-91 *Right foot (lateral view).*

1 Calcaneus (lateral surface)	7 Lateral tubercle of talus	17 2nd Metatarsal
2 Lateral process of calcaneal tuberosity	8 Neck of talus	18 3rd Metatarsal
3 Fibular trochlea	9 Head of talus	19 4th Metatarsal
4 Groove for distal tendon of fibularis longus muscle	10 Navicular	20 5th Metatarsal
5 Tarsal sinus	11 Cuboid	21 Tuberosity of base of 5th metatarsal
6 Articular surface of talus for (lateral malleolus of) ankle joint	12 Groove for distal tendon of fibularis longus muscle	22 Proximal phalanx of big toe
	13 1st Cuneiform	23 Distal phalanx of big toe
	14 2nd Cuneiform	24 Proximal phalanx of little toe
	15 3rd Cuneiform	25 Middle phalanx of little toe
	16 1st Metatarsal	26 Distal phalanx of little toe

PART 3

Internal Anatomy

1 Left frontal sinus
2 Left ethmoidal air cells
3 Falx cerebri
4 Medial surface of right cerebral hemisphere
5 Anterior cerebral artery
6 Corpus callosum
7 Arachnoid granulations
8 Superior sagittal sinus
9 Tentorium cerebelli
10 Straight sinus
11 Cerebellum
12 Great cerebral vein
13 Midbrain
14 Pons
15 Fourth ventricle
16 Medulla oblongata
17 Margin of foramen magnum
18 Cerebellomedullary cistern (cisterna magna)
19 Posterior arch of atlas
20 Spinal cord
21 Intervertebral disk between axis and third cervical vertebra
22 Laryngopharynx
23 Inlet of larynx
24 Thyroid cartilage
25 Hyoid bone
26 Epiglottis
27 Vallecula
28 Oropharynx
29 Tongue
30 Mandible
31 Hard palate
32 Soft palate
33 Nasopharynx
34 Dens of axis
35 Anterior arch of atlas
36 Pharyngeal tonsil
37 Opening of auditory tube
38 Choana (posterior nasal aperture)
39 Nasal septum
40 Sphenoidal sinus
41 Pituitary gland
42 Optic chiasma

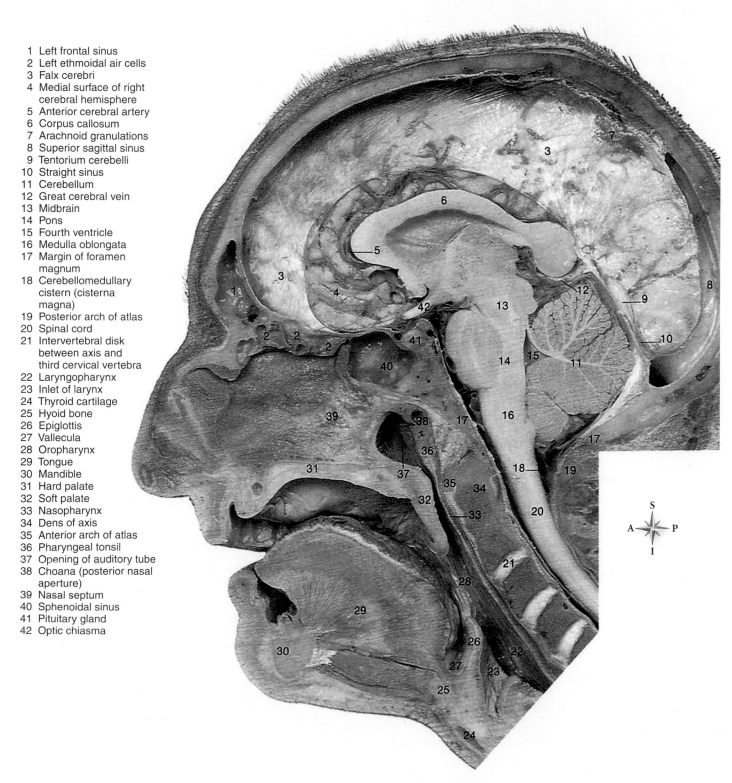

Figure 3-1 *Right half of the head, in sagittal section (lateral view).*

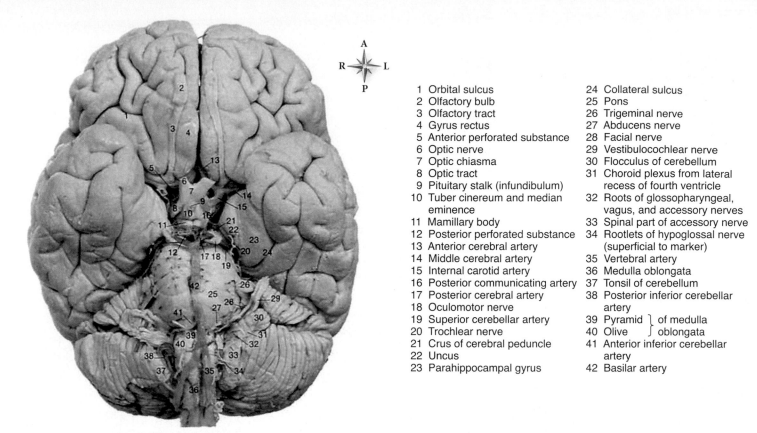

1 Orbital sulcus
2 Olfactory bulb
3 Olfactory tract
4 Gyrus rectus
5 Anterior perforated substance
6 Optic nerve
7 Optic chiasma
8 Optic tract
9 Pituitary stalk (infundibulum)
10 Tuber cinereum and median eminence
11 Mamillary body
12 Posterior perforated substance
13 Anterior cerebral artery
14 Middle cerebral artery
15 Internal carotid artery
16 Posterior communicating artery
17 Posterior cerebral artery
18 Oculomotor nerve
19 Superior cerebellar artery
20 Trochlear nerve
21 Crus of cerebral peduncle
22 Uncus
23 Parahippocampal gyrus

24 Collateral sulcus
25 Pons
26 Trigeminal nerve
27 Abducens nerve
28 Facial nerve
29 Vestibulocochlear nerve
30 Flocculus of cerebellum
31 Choroid plexus from lateral recess of fourth ventricle
32 Roots of glossopharyngeal, vagus, and accessory nerves
33 Spinal part of accessory nerve
34 Rootlets of hypoglossal nerve (superficial to marker)
35 Vertebral artery
36 Medulla oblongata
37 Tonsil of cerebellum
38 Posterior inferior cerebellar artery
39 Pyramid ⎱ of medulla
40 Olive ⎰ oblongata
41 Anterior inferior cerebellar artery
42 Basilar artery

Figure 3-2 *Brain (inferior view).*

1 Anterior cerebral artery
2 Rostrum ⎫
3 Genu   ⎬ of corpus callosum
4 Body   ⎭
5 Cingulate gyrus
6 Precentral gyrus
7 Central sulcus
8 Postcentral gyrus
9 Parietooccipital sulcus
10 Calcarine sulcus
11 Lingual gyrus
12 Cerebellum
13 Medulla oblongata
14 Median aperture of fourth ventricle
15 Fourth ventricle
16 Pons
17 Basilar artery
18 Tegmentum ⎫
19 Aqueduct ⎬ of midbrain
20 Inferior colliculu ⎥
21 Superior colliculus ⎭
22 Posterior commissure
23 Pineal body
24 Suprapineal recess
25 Great cerebral vein
26 Splenium of corpus callosum

27 Fornix
28 Cut edge of septum pellucidum
29 Body of lateral ventricle
30 Thalamus
31 Interthalamic connection
32 Hypothalamic sulcus
33 Hypothalamus
34 Posterior perforated substance
35 Mamillary body
36 Tuber cinereum and median eminence
37 Infundibular recess (base of pituitary stalk)
38 Optic chiasma
39 Supraoptic recess
40 Lamina terminalis
41 Anterior commissure
42 Anterior column of fornix
43 Interventricular foramen and choroid plexus

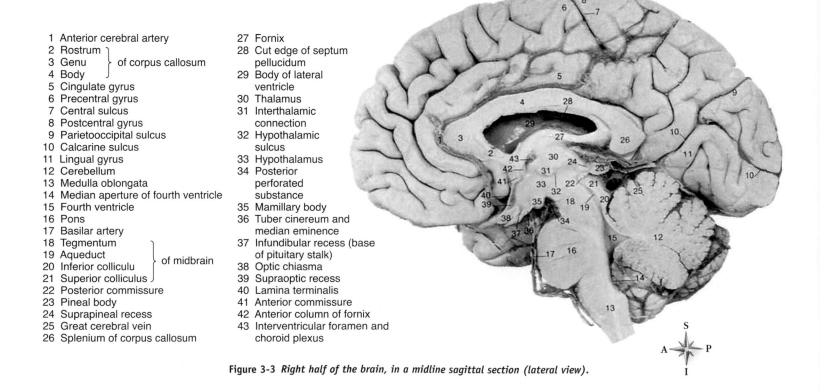

Figure 3-3 *Right half of the brain, in a midline sagittal section (lateral view).*

1   Petrous part of temporal bone
2   Tentorium cerebelli
3   Inferior ⎫
4   Middle ⎬ cerebellar peduncle
5   Superior ⎭
6   Superior medullary velum
7   Trochlear nerve
8   Inferior ⎫ colliculus
9   Superior ⎭
10 Straight sinus
11 Medial eminence
12 Facial colliculus
13 Medullary striae
14 Facial and vestibulocochlear nerves and internal acoustic meatus
15 Glossopharyngeal, vagus, and accessory nerves and jugular foramen
16 Spinal part of accessory nerve
17 Rootlets of hypoglossal nerve and hypoglossal canal
18 Margin of foramen magnum
19 Vertebral artery
20 Lateral mass of atlas
21 Ventral ramus of first cervical nerve
22 Dorsal rootlets ⎫
23 Dorsal root ganglion ⎬ of second
24 Ventral ramus ⎬ cervical nerve
25 Dorsal ramus ⎭
26 Posterior belly of digastric muscle
27 Internal jugular vein
28 Zygapophyseal joint
29 Spinal cord
30 Denticulate ligament
31 Dura mater
32 Sympathetic trunk
33 Common carotid artery
34 Vagus nerve
35 Internal carotid artery
36 Superior cervical sympathetic ganglion
37 Hypoglossal nerve

Figure 3-4 *Brainstem and upper part of the spinal cord (posterior view).*

1 Conus medullaris of spinal cord
2 Cauda equina
3 Dura mater
4 Superior articular process of
   third lumbar vertebra
5 Filum terminale
6 Roots of fifth lumbar nerve
7 Fourth lumbar intervertebral disk
8 Pedicle of fifth lumbar vertebra
9 Dorsal root ganglion of fifth
   lumbar nerve
10 Fifth lumbar (lumbosacral) vertebra
11 Dural sheath of first sacral nerve
    roots
12 Lateral part of sacrum
13 Second sacral vertebra

Figure 3-5 *Vertebral column, lumbar and sacral regions (posterior view).*

1 Lateral cord
2 Posterior cord
3 Medial cord
4 Pectoralis minor and lateral pectoral nerve
5 Musculocutaneous nerve
6 Axillary nerve
7 Lateral root of median nerve
8 Radial nerve
9 Medial root of median nerve
10 Upper subscapular nerves
11 Thoracodorsal nerve
12 Lower subscapular nerve
13 Medial cutaneous nerve of arm
14 Ulnar nerve
15 Medial cutaneous nerve of forearm
16 Intercostobrachial nerve
17 Subscapularis
18 Teres major
19 Latissimus dorsi
20 Long head of triceps
21 Lateral head of triceps
22 Medial head of triceps
23 Radial nerve branches to triceps
24 Median nerve
25 Coracobrachialis
26 Biceps
27 Deltoid

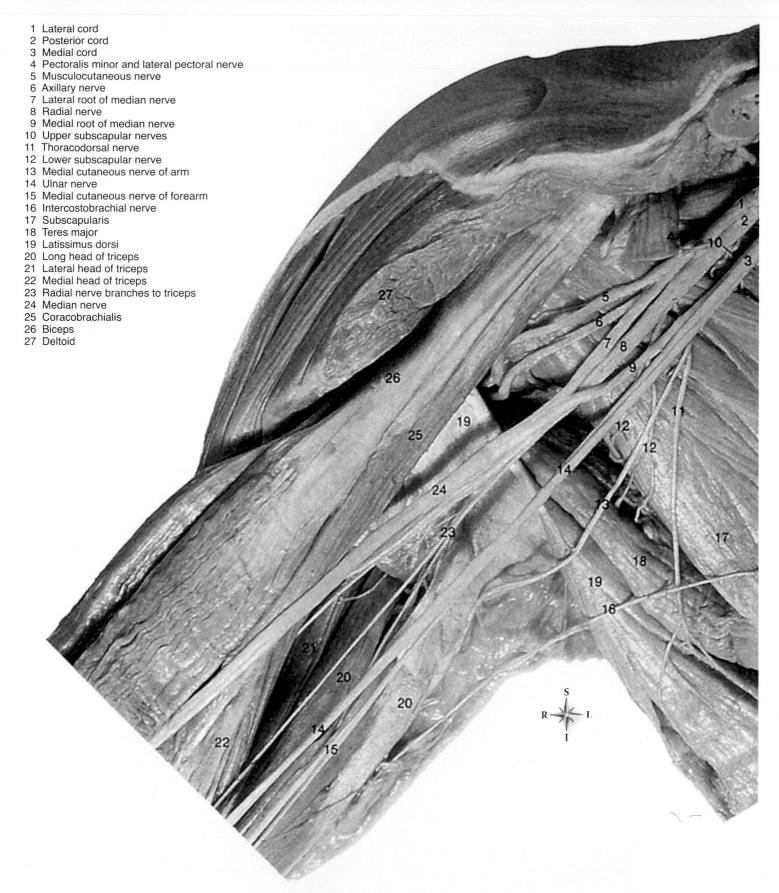

Figure 3-6 *Right brachial plexus and branches (anterior view).*

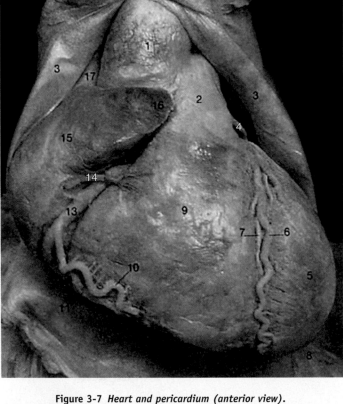

1 Ascending aorta
2 Pulmonary trunk
3 Serous pericardium overlying fibrous
   pericardium (turned laterally)
4 Auricle of left atrium
5 Left ventricle
6 Anterior interventricular branch of left
   coronary artery
7 Great cardiac vein
8 Diaphragm
9 Right ventricle
10 Marginal branch of right coronary artery
11 Small cardiac vein
12 Pericardium fused with tendon of diaphragm
13 Right coronary artery
14 Anterior cardiac vein
15 Right atrium
16 Auricle of right atrium
17 Superior vena cava

Figure 3-7 *Heart and pericardium (anterior view).*

1 Arch of cricoid cartilage
2 Isthmus   ⎤ of thyroid
3 Lateral lobe ⎦ gland
4 Trachea
5 Inferior thyroid veins
6 Left common carotid artery
7 Left vagus nerve
8 Internal jugular vein
9 Subclavian vein
10 Thoracic duct
11 Internal thoracic vein
12 Internal thoracic artery
13 Phrenic nerve
14 Parietal pleura (cut edge) over lung
15 Left brachiocephalic vein
16 A thymic artery
17 Thymic veins
18 Thymus
19 Superior vena cava
20 Right brachiocephalic vein
21 First rib
22 Brachiocephalic trunk
23 Right common carotid artery
24 Right subclavian artery
25 Right recurrent laryngeal nerve
26 Right vagus nerve
27 Unusual cervical tributary of 20
28 Vertebral vein
29 Thyrocervical trunk
30 Suprascapular artery
31 Scalenus anterior
32 Upper trunk of brachial plexus
33 Superficial cervical artery
34 Ascending cervical artery
35 Inferior thyroid artery
36 Sympathetic trunk

Figure 3-8 *Thoracic inlet and mediastinum (anterior view).*

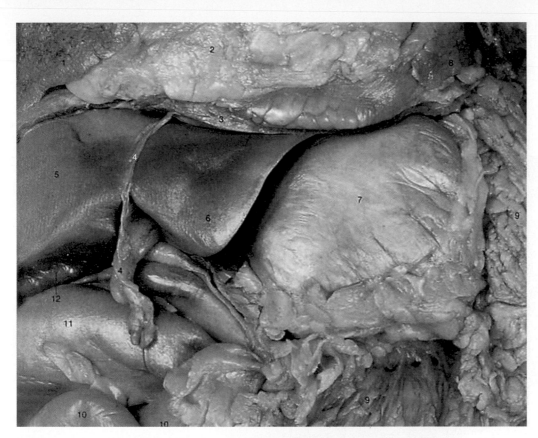

1 Inferior lobe of right lung
2 Pericardial fat
3 Diaphragm
4 Falciform ligament
5 Right lobe of liver
6 Left lobe of liver
7 Stomach
8 Inferior lobe of left lung
9 Greater omentum
10 Small intestine
11 Transverse colon
12 Gallbladder

Figure 3-9 *Upper abdominal viscera (anterior view).*

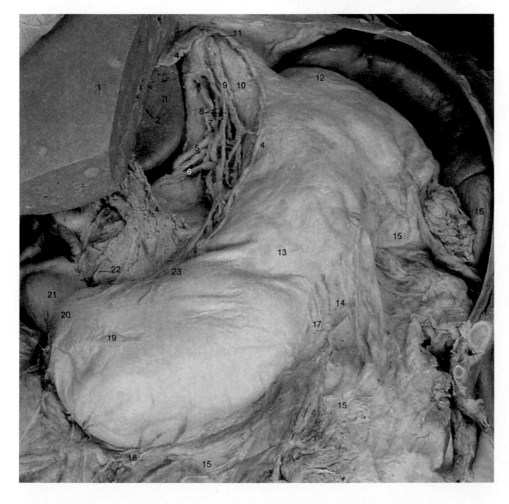

1 Right lobe of liver
2 Fissure of ligamentum venosum
3 Caudate lobe of liver
4 Lesser omentum (cut edge)
5 Left gastric artery
6 Left gastric vein
7 Posterior vagal trunk
8 Esophageal branches of left gastric vessels
9 Anterior vagal trunk
10 Esophagus
11 Esophageal opening in diaphragm
12 Fundus ⎫
13 Body   ⎬ of stomach
14 Greater curvature ⎭
15 Greater omentum
16 Lower end of spleen
17 Branches of left gastroepiploic vessels
18 Right gastroepiploic vessels and branches
19 Pyloric part of stomach
20 Pylorus
21 Superior (first) part of duodenum
22 Right gastric artery
23 Lesser curvature

Figure 3-10 *Stomach, with vessels and vagus nerves (anterior view).*

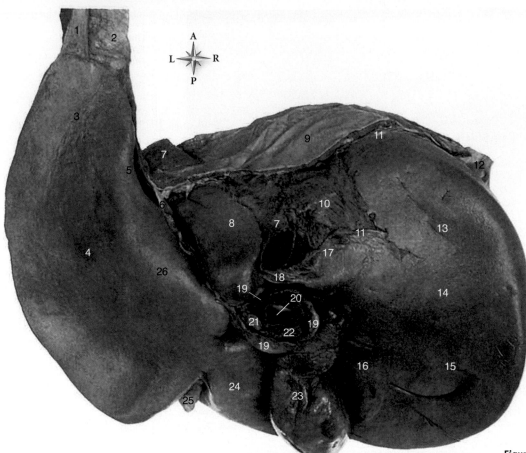

1 Left triangular ligament
2 Diaphragm
3 Left lobe
4 Gastric impression
5 Esophageal groove
6 Lesser omentum in fissure for ligamentum venosum
7 Inferior vena cava
8 Caudate lobe
9 Diaphragm on part of bare area
10 Bare area
11 Inferior layer of coronary ligament
12 Right triangular ligament
13 Renal impression
14 Right lobe
15 Colic impression
16 Duodenal impression
17 Suprarenal impression
18 Caudate process
19 Right free margin of lesser omentum in porta hepatis
20 Portal vein
21 Hepatic artery
22 Common hepatic duct
23 Gallbladder
24 Quadrate lobe
25 Ligamentum teres and falciform ligament in fissure for legamentum teres
26 Omental tuberosity

Figure 3-11 *Liver (from above and behind).*

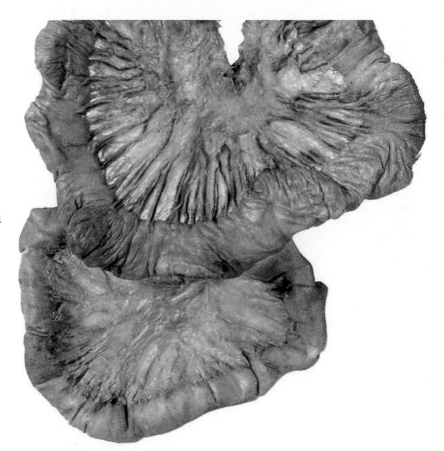

Figure 3-12 *Small intestine.* Coil of typical jejunum, coil of typical ileum.

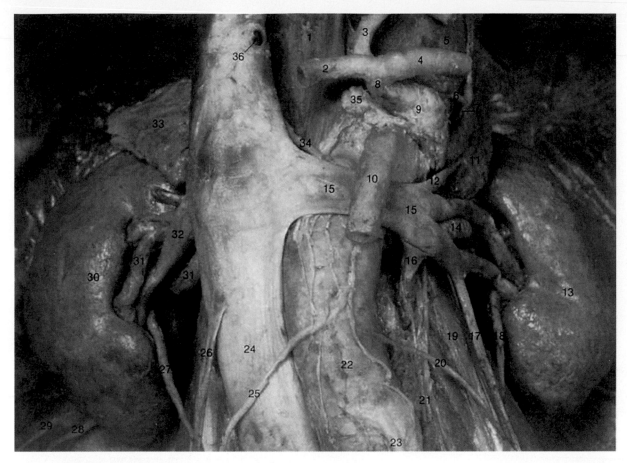

1 Right crus of diaphragm
2 Common hepatic artery
3 Left gastric artery
4 Splenic artery
5 Left crus of diaphragm
6 Left inferior phrenic artery
7 Left inferior phrenic vein
8 Celiac trunk
9 Left celiac ganglion
10 Superior mesenteric artery
11 Left suprarenal gland
12 Left suprarenal vein
13 Left kidney
14 Left renal artery
15 Left renal vein
16 Lumbar tributary of renal vein
17 Left gonadal vein
18 Left ureter

19 Left psoas major
20 Left gonadal artery
21 Left sympathetic trunk
22 Abdominal aorta and aortic plexus
23 Inferior mesenteric artery
24 Inferior vena cava
25 Right gonadal artery
26 Right gonadal vein
27 Right ureter
28 Right ilioinguinal nerve
29 Right iliohypogastric nerve
30 Right kidney
31 Right renal artery
32 Right renal vein
33 Right suprarenal gland
34 Right inferior phrenic artery
35 Right celiac ganglion
36 A hepatic vein

Figure 3-13 *Kidneys and suprarenal glands (anterior view).*

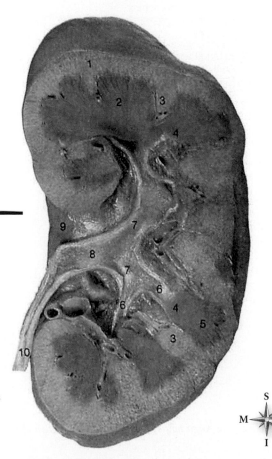

1 Cortex
2 Medulla
3 Renal column
4 Renal papilla
5 Medullary pyramid
6 Minor calyx
7 Major calyx
8 Renal pelvis
9 Hilum
10 Ureter

Figure 3-14 *Kidney.* Internal structure in frontal section.

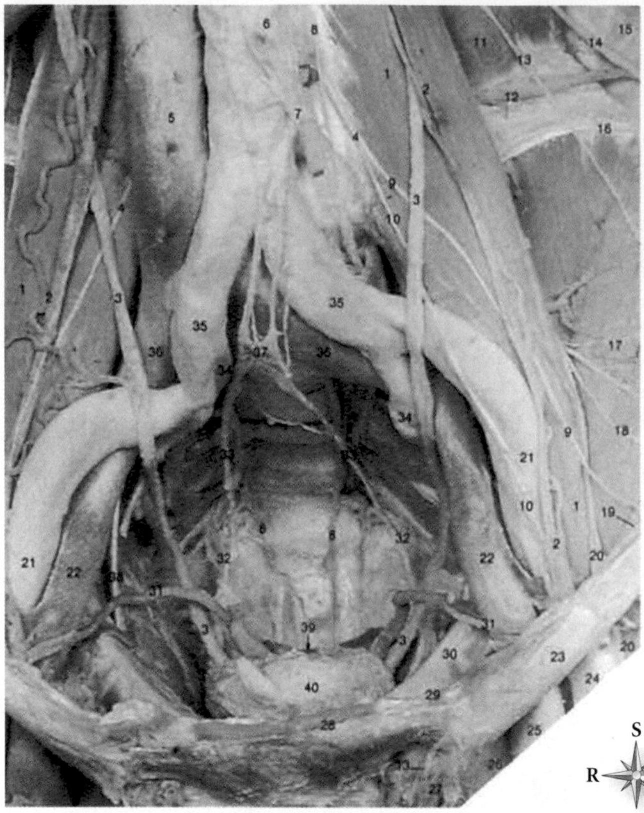

1 Psoas major
2 Testicular vessels
3 Ureter
4 Genitofemoral nerve
5 Inferior vena cava
6 Aorta and aortic plexus
7 Inferior mesenteric artery and plexus
8 Sympathetic trunk and ganglia
9 Femoral } branch of
10 Genital } genitofemoral nerve
11 Quadratus lumborum
12 Fourth lumbar artery
13 Ilioinguinal nerve
14 Iliohypogastric nerve
15 Lumbar part of thoracolumbar fascia
16 Iliolumbar ligament
17 Iliacus and branches from femoral nerve and iliolumbar artery
18 Lateral femoral cutaneous nerve arising from femoral nerve
19 Deep circumflex iliac artery
20 Femoral nerve
21 External iliac artery
22 External iliac vein
23 Inguinal ligament
24 Femoral artery
25 Femoral vein
26 Position of femoral canal
27 Spermatic cord
28 Rectus abdominis
29 Lacunar ligament
30 Pectineal ligament
31 Ductus deferens
32 Inferior hypogastric (pelvic) plexus and pelvic splanchnic nerves
33 Hypogastric nerve
34 Internal iliac artery
35 Common iliac artery
36 Common iliac vein
37 Superior hypogastric plexus
38 Obturator nerve and vessels
39 Rectum (cut edge)
40 Bladder

Figure 3-15 ***Posterior abdominal and pelvic walls (anterior view).***

1 Rectus abdominis
2 Extraperitoneal fat
3 Sigmoid colon
4 Promontory of sacrum
5 Rectum
6 Coccyx
7 Anococcygeal body
8 External anal sphincter
9 Anal canal with anal columns of mucous membrane
10 Perineal body
11 Ductus deferens
12 Epididymis
13 Testis
14 Spongy part of urethra and corpus spongiosum
15 Corpus cavernosum
16 Bulbospongiosus
17 Perineal membrane
18 Sphincter urethrae
19 Membranous part of urethra
20 Pubic symphysis
21 Prostate
22 Prostatic part of urethra
23 Seminal colliculus
24 Bristle in ejaculatory duct
25 Internal urethral orifice
26 Bladder
27 Bristle passing up into right ureteral orifice
28 Rectovesical pouch
29 Puborectalis fibers of levator ani

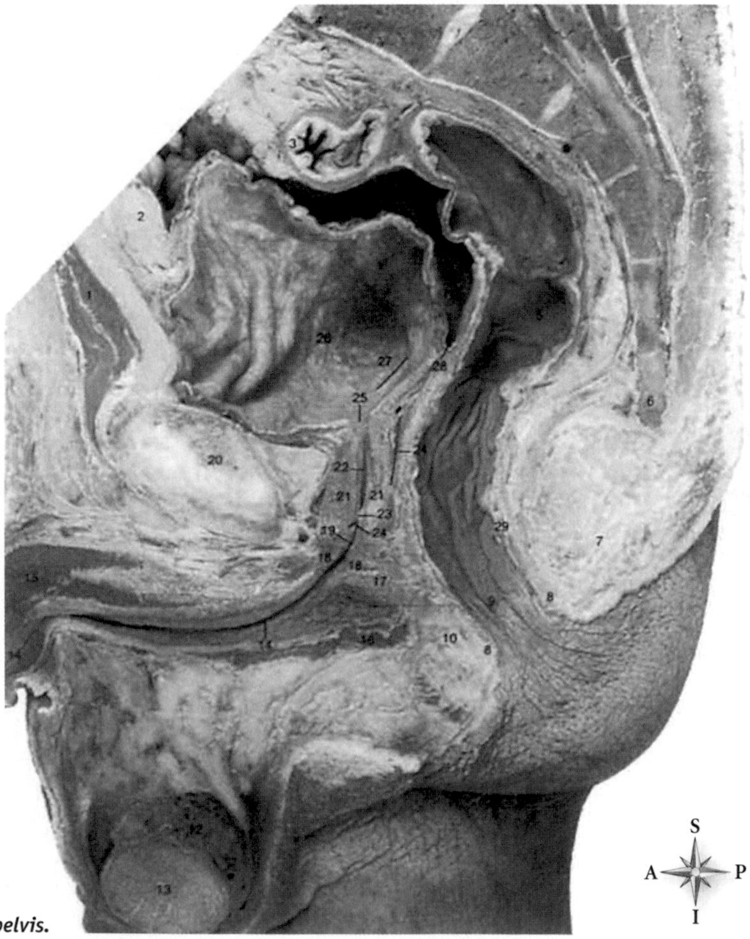

Figure 3-16 ***Right half of a midline sagittal section of the male pelvis.***

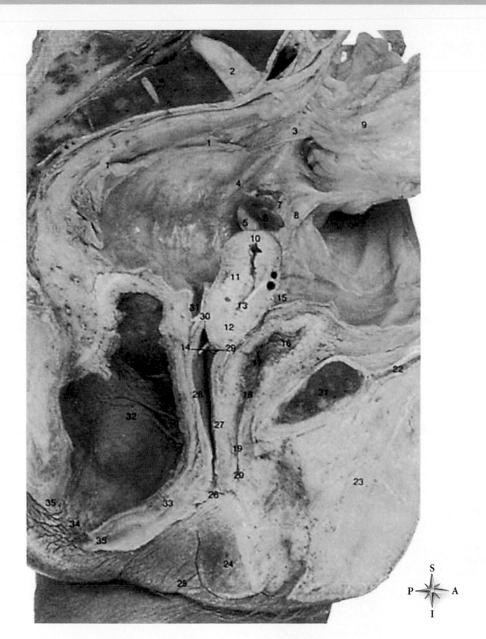

1 Line of attachment of right limb
   of sigmoid mesocolon
2 Fifth lumbar intervertebral disk
3 Apex of sigmoid mesocolon
4 Ureter underlying peritoneum
5 Ovary
6 Uterine tube
7 Suspensory ligament of ovary
   containing ovarian vessels
8 Left limb of sigmoid mesocolon
   overlying external iliac vessels
9 Sigmoid colon (reflected to left
   and upwards)
10 Fundus ⎤
11 Body ⎬ of uterus
12 Cervix ⎦
13 Marker in internal os
14 Marker in external os
15 Vesico-uterine pouch
16 Bladder

17 Marker in left ureteral orifice
18 Internal urethral orifice
19 Urethra
20 External urethral orifice
21 Pubic symphysis
22 Rectus abdominis (turned
   forwards)
23 Fat of mons pubis
24 Labium minus
25 Labium majus
26 Vestibule
27 Anterior wall ⎤
28 Posterior wall ⎬ of vagina
29 Anterior fornix
30 Posterior fornix ⎦
31 Recto-uterine pouch
32 Rectum
33 Perineal body
34 Anal canal
35 External anal sphincter

Figure 3-17 *Left half of a midline sagittal section of the female pelvis.*

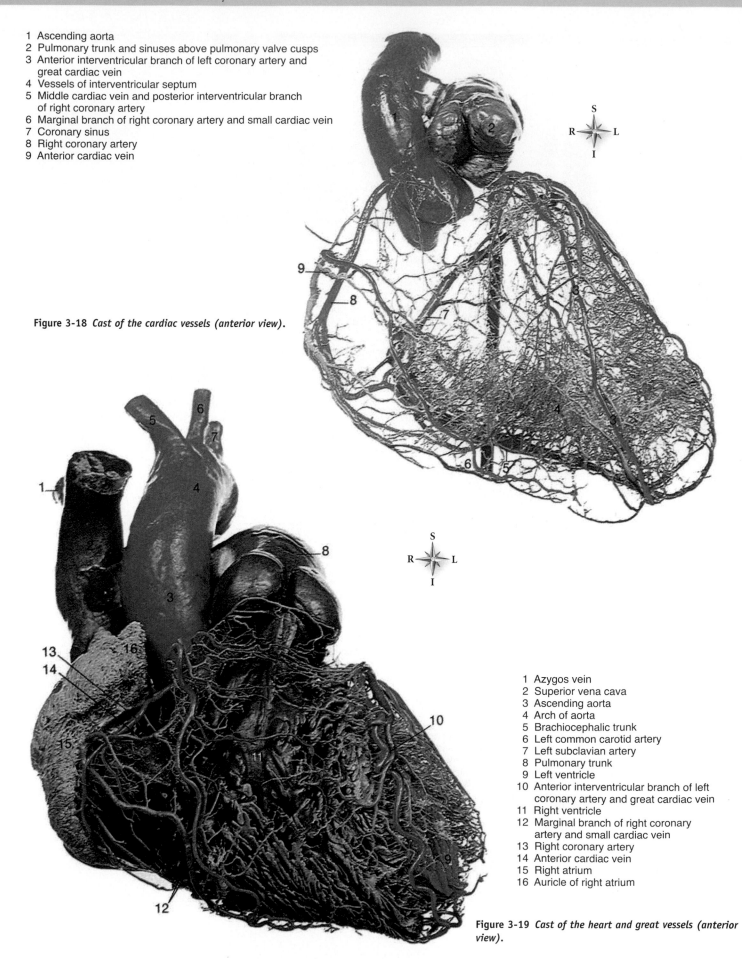

1 Ascending aorta
2 Pulmonary trunk and sinuses above pulmonary valve cusps
3 Anterior interventricular branch of left coronary artery and great cardiac vein
4 Vessels of interventricular septum
5 Middle cardiac vein and posterior interventricular branch of right coronary artery
6 Marginal branch of right coronary artery and small cardiac vein
7 Coronary sinus
8 Right coronary artery
9 Anterior cardiac vein

Figure 3-18 *Cast of the cardiac vessels (anterior view).*

1 Azygos vein
2 Superior vena cava
3 Ascending aorta
4 Arch of aorta
5 Brachiocephalic trunk
6 Left common carotid artery
7 Left subclavian artery
8 Pulmonary trunk
9 Left ventricle
10 Anterior interventricular branch of left coronary artery and great cardiac vein
11 Right ventricle
12 Marginal branch of right coronary artery and small cardiac vein
13 Right coronary artery
14 Anterior cardiac vein
15 Right atrium
16 Auricle of right atrium

Figure 3-19 *Cast of the heart and great vessels (anterior view).*

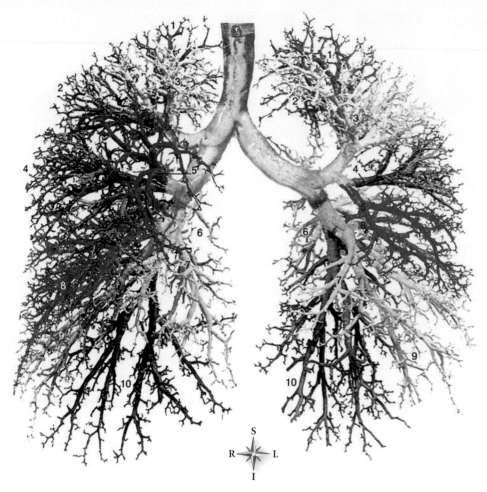

RIGHT LUNG
Superior lobe
 1 Apical
 2 Posterior
 3 Anterior

Middle lobe
 4 Lateral
 5 Medial

Inferior lobe
 6 Apical (superior)
 7 Medial basal
 8 Anterior basal
 9 Lateral basal
10 Posterior basal

LEFT LUNG
Superior lobe
 1 Apical
 2 Posterior
 3 Anterior
 4 Superior lingular
 5 Inferior lingular

Inferior lobe
 6 Apical (superior)
 7 Medial basal (cardiac)
 8 Anterior basal
 9 Lateral basal
10 Posterior basal

Figure 3-20 *Cast of the bronchial tree (anterior view).*

 1 Right branch of portal vein and hepatic
    artery and right hepatic duct
 2 Gallbladder
 3 Bile duct
 4 Hepatic artery
 5 Portal vein
 6 Left branch of portal vein and hepatic
    artery and left hepatic duct
 7 Left gastric artery
 8 Left gastric vein
 9 Splenic artery
10 Splenic vein
11 Short gastric vessels
12 Left gastroepiploic vessels
13 Vessels of left kidney
14 Pancreatic duct
15 Duodenojejunal flexure
16 Superior mesenteric artery
17 Superior mesenteric vein
18 Horizontal (third) part of duodenum
19 Right gastroepiploic vessels
20 Pyloric canal
21 Pylorus
22 Superior (first) part of duodenum
23 Right gastric vessels
24 Branches of superior and inferior
    pancreaticoduodenal vessels
25 Descending (second) part of duodenum
26 Vessels of right kidney

Figure 3-21 *Cast of the duodenum, liver, biliary tract, and associated vessels (anterior view).*

1 Right renal vein
2 Right suprarenal vein
3 Inferior vena cava
4 Aorta
5 Celiac trunk
6 Superior mesenteric
  artery

7 Left renal vein
8 Left suprarenal veins
9 Left renal artery
10 Accessory renal
   arteries
11 Right renal artery

Figure 3-22 *Cast of the kidneys and great vessels (anterior view).*

PART 4

Cross-Sectional Anatomy

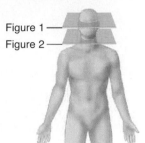

Figure 1
Figure 2

1 Arytenoid cartilage
2 Claustrum
3 Common carotid artery
4 Ethmoidal air cells
5 Head of caudate nucleus
6 Internal capsule of cerebrum
7 Internal jugular vein
8 Lamina of vertebra
9 Lateral rectus muscle
10 Lens
11 Lentiform nucleus
12 Levator scapulae muscle
13 Ligamentum nuchae
14 Longus colli muscle
15 Medial rectus muscle
16 Nasal cavity
17 Optic canal
18 Optic chiasma
19 Optic nerve
20 Optic radiation
21 Orbital fat
22 Piriform fossa, pharynx
23 Platysma muscle
24 Scalenus anterior muscle
25 Scalenus medius and scalenus posterior
26 Semispinalis capitis muscle
27 Spinal cord
28 Spinalis muscle
29 Splenius capitis muscle
30 Sternocleidomastoid muscle
31 Superior sagittal sinus
32 Temporal lobe, cerebrum
33 Temporalis muscle
34 Thalamus
35 Thyroid cartilage
36 Thyroid gland, lateral lobe
37 Trapezius muscle
38 Vertebral artery in transverse foramen
39 Vertebral body
40 Vertebral canal
41 Vocal cord
42 Zygomatic bone

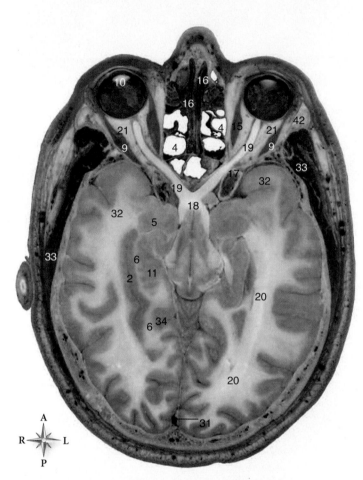

Figure 4-1 *Head and neck (inferior view).* Cross section at level of optic chiasma.

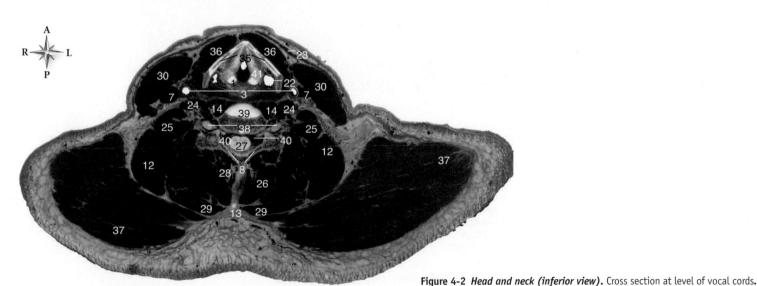

Figure 4-2 *Head and neck (inferior view).* Cross section at level of vocal cords.

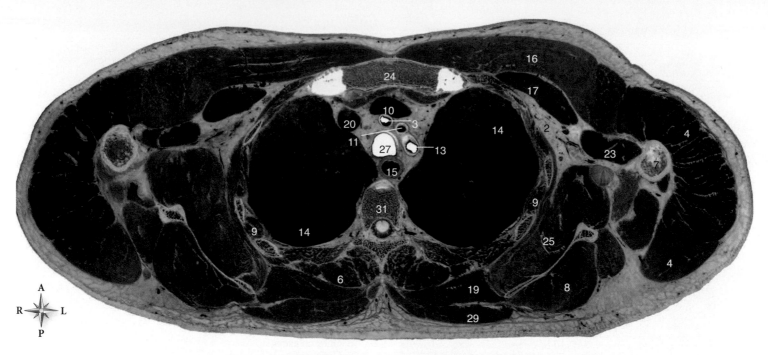

Figure 4-3 *Thorax (inferior view).* Cross section at T2 vertebral level.

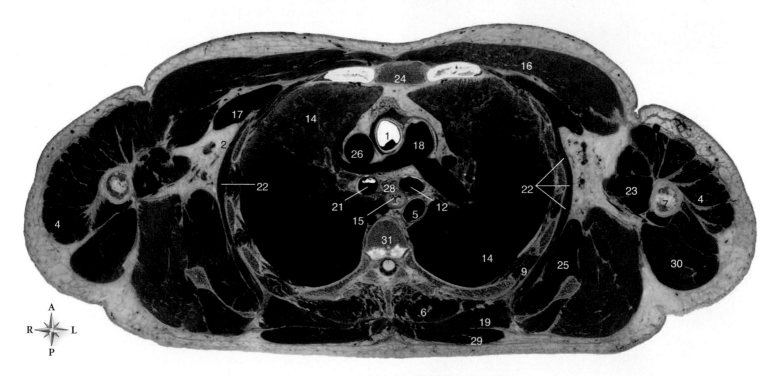

1 Ascending aorta
2 Axillary fat with brachial plexus
3 Brachiocephalic artery
4 Deltoid muscle
5 Descending aorta
6 Erector spinae muscle
7 Humerus
8 Infraspinatus muscle
9 Intercostal muscles
10 Left brachiocephalic vein
11 Left common carotid artery

12 Left main bronchus
13 Left subclavian artery
14 Lung
15 Esophagus
16 Pectoralis major muscle
17 Pectoralis minor muscle
18 Pulmonary trunk
19 Rhomboid major muscle
20 Right brachiocephalic vein
21 Right main bronchus
22 Serratus anterior muscle

23 Short head of biceps brachii
24 Sternal marrow
25 Subscapularis muscle
26 Superior vena cava
27 Trachea
28 Tracheobronchial lymph
29 Trapezius muscle
30 Triceps muscle
31 Vertebral body

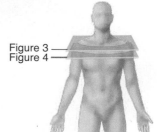

Figure 3
Figure 4

Figure 4-4 *Thorax (inferior view).* Cross section at T4 vertebral level.

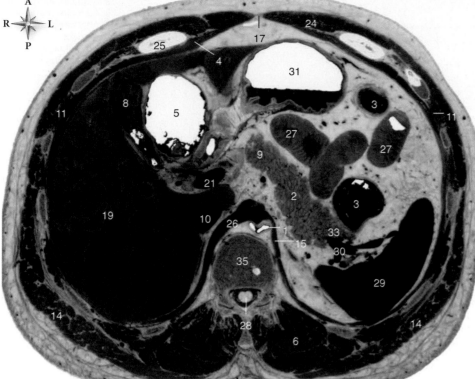

1 Aorta
2 Body of pancreas
3 Descending colon
4 Diaphragm
5 Duodenum
6 Erector spinae muscle
7 External oblique muscle
8 Gallbladder
9 Head of pancreas
10 Inferior vena cava
11 Intercostal muscle
12 Intervertebral disk
13 Kidney
14 Latissimus dorsi muscle
15 Left crus of diaphragm
16 Left renal vein
17 Linea alba
18 Linea semilunaris
19 Liver
20 Perirenal fat
21 Portal vein
22 Psoas muscle
23 Quadratus abdominis muscle
24 Rectus abdominis muscle
25 Rib
26 Right crus of diaphragm
27 Small intestine
28 Spinal cord
29 Spleen
30 Splenic artery and vein
31 Stomach
32 Superior mesenteric vessels
33 Tail of pancreas
34 Transverse colon
35 Vertebral body

Figure 4-5 *Abdomen (inferior view).* Cross section at L1 vertebral level.

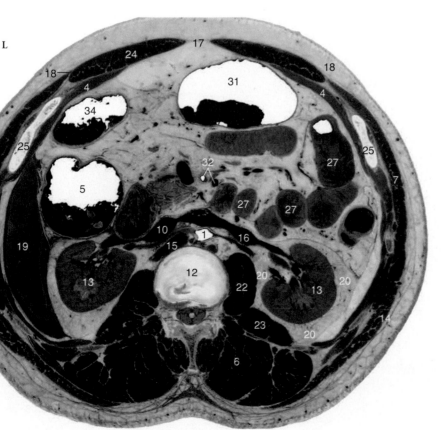

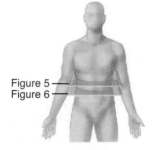

Figure 4-6 *Abdomen (inferior view).* Cross section at L2 vertebral level.

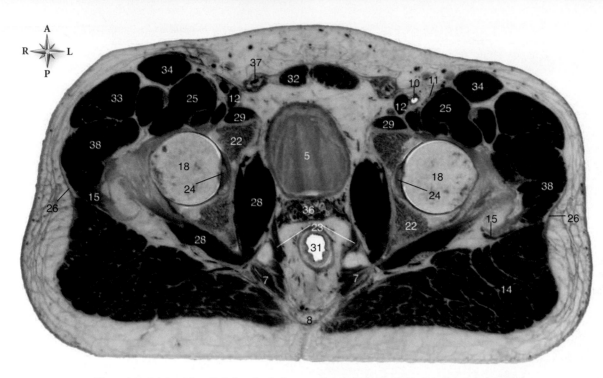

1 Adductor brevis muscle
2 Adductor longus muscle
3 Adductor magnus muscle
4 Anal canal
5 Bladder
6 Bulb of penis
7 Coccygeus part of levator
   ani muscle
8 Coccyx
9 Crus of penis
10 Femoral artery
11 Femoral nerve
12 Femoral vein
13 Femur
14 Gluteus maximus muscle
15 Gluteus minimus muscle
16 Great saphenous vein
17 Hamstring origin
18 Head of femur
19 Ischiocavernosus
20 Ischial tuberosity
21 Ischioanal fossa
22 Ischium
23 Levator ani muscle
24 Ligament of head of femur
25 Iliopsoas muscle
26 Iliotibial tract
27 Obturator externus muscle
28 Obturator internus muscle
29 Pectineus muscle
30 Quadratus femoris muscle
31 Rectum
32 Rectus abdominis muscle
33 Rectus femoris muscle
34 Sartorius muscle
35 Sciatic nerve
36 Seminal vesicles
37 Spermatic cord
38 Tensor fasciae latae muscle
39 Vastus intermedius muscle
40 Vastus lateralis muscle

Figure 4-7 *Pelvic region (inferior view).* Cross section at level of the hip joint in a male pelvis.

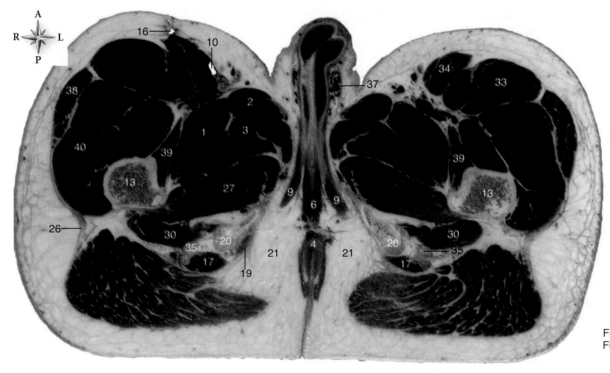

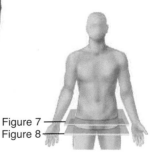

Figure 7
Figure 8

Figure 4-8 *Pelvic region (inferior view).* Cross section at level of the upper thigh in a male pelvis.

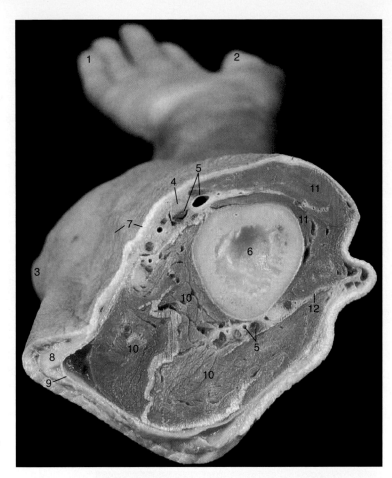

1 Digit 5 (little finger)
2 Digit 1 (thumb)
3 Medial epicondyle (surface bump)
4 Nerve
5 Blood vessels
6 Humerus
7 Skin
8 Superficial fascia
9 Deep fascia
10 Muscles of the posterior compartment
11 Muscles of the anterior compartment
12 Lateral intermuscular septum

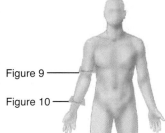

Figure 9

Figure 10

Figure 4-9 *Upper arm.* Cross section proximal to the elbow.

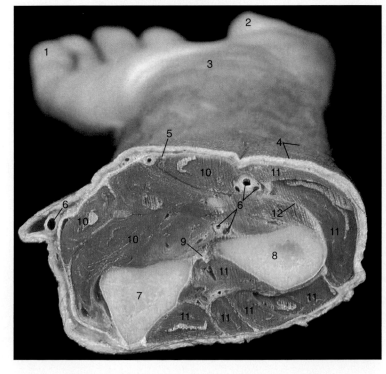

1 Digit 5 (little finger)
2 Digit 1 (thumb)
3 Carpus (wrist)
4 Skin
5 Deep fascia
6 Blood vessels
7 Ulna
8 Radius
9 Interosseus ligament
10 Muscles of the anterior compartment
11 Muscles of the posterior compartment
12 Intermuscular septum

Figure 4-10 *Lower arm.* Cross section distal to the elbow.

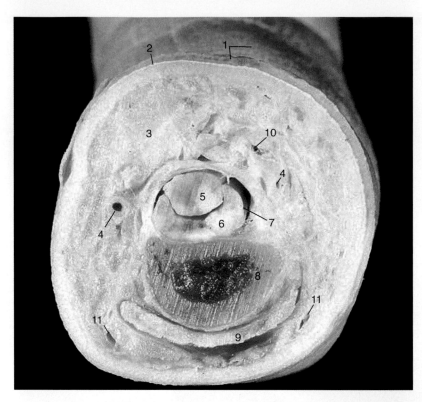

1 Epidermis
2 Dermis
3 Superficial fascia
4 Digital artery
5 Tendon (flexor digitorum superficialis)
6 Tendon (flexor digitorum profundis)
7 Tendon sheath
8 Proximal phalanx
9 Tendon (extensor expansion)
10 Digital nerve
11 Digital vein

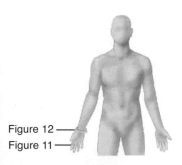

Figure 4-11 *Second digit (index finger).* Cross section at the proximal phalanx.

Figure 12
Figure 11

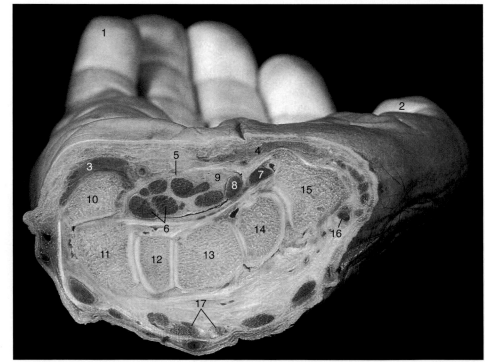

1 Digit 5 (little finger)
2 Digit 1 (thumb)
3 Hypothenar muscles
4 Thenar muscles
5 Tendon sheath (of carpal tunnel)
6 Tendons (digital flexor)
7 Flexor carpi radialis
8 Flexor pollicis longus
9 Median nerve
10 Pisiform
11 Triquetral
12 Hamate
13 Capitate
14 Trapezoid
15 Trapezium
16 Radial artery
17 Tendons (digital extensor)

Figure 4-12 *Carpus (wrist).* Cross section showing the carpal tunnel.

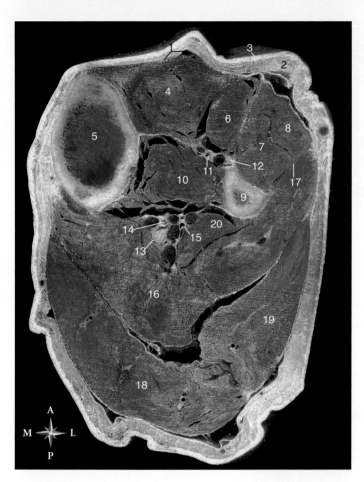

1 Deep fascia
2 Superficial fascia
3 Skin
4 Tibialis anterior
5 Tibia
6 Extensor digitorum longus
7 Peroneus brevis
8 Peroneus longus
9 Fibula
10 Tibialis posterior
11 Anterior tibial artery
12 Deep peroneal nerve
13 Tibial nerve
14 Posterior tibial artery
15 Peroneal artery
16 Soleus
17 Posterior peroneal intermuscular septum
18 Gastrocnemius (medial head)
19 Gastrocnemius (lateral head)
20 Flexor hallucis longus

Figure 4-13 *Leg.* Cross section showing bones and muscles below the knee.

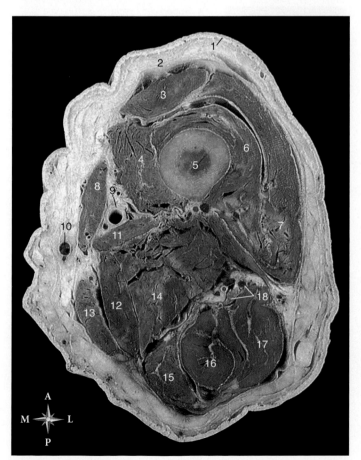

1 Skin
2 Superficial fascia
3 Rectus femoris
4 Vastus medialis
5 Femur
6 Vastus intermedius
7 Vastus lateralis
8 Sartorius
9 Femoral artery
10 Great saphenous vein
11 Adductor longus
12 Adductor brevis
13 Gracilis
14 Adductor magnus
15 Semimembranosus
16 Semitendinosus
17 Biceps femoris
18 Branches of sciatic nerve

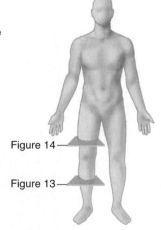

Figure 4-14 *Thigh.* Cross section showing major muscles above the knee.

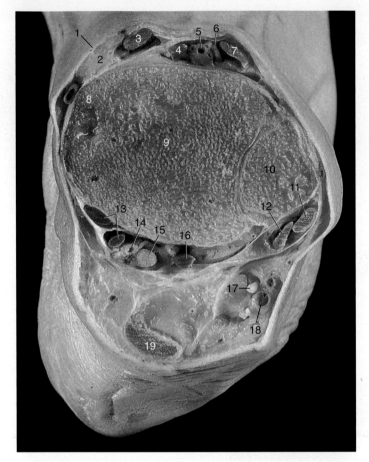

1 Skin
2 Superficial fascia
3 Tendon (tibialis anterior)
4 Tendon (extensor hallucis longus)
5 Anterior tibial artery
6 Deep peroneal nerve
7 Tendon (extensor digitorum longus)
8 Great saphenous vein
9 Tibia
10 Lateral malleolus of fibula
11 Tendon (peroneus longus)
12 Tendon (peroneus brevis)
13 Tendons (tibialis posterior, flexor digitorum longus)
14 Posterior tibial artery
15 Posterior tibial nerve
16 Tendon (flexor hallucis longus)
17 Sural nerve
18 Short saphenous vein
19 Tendon (calcaneal or Achilles)

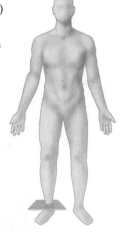

Figure 4-15 *Lower leg.* Cross section just above the ankle joint cavity, showing relations of structures.

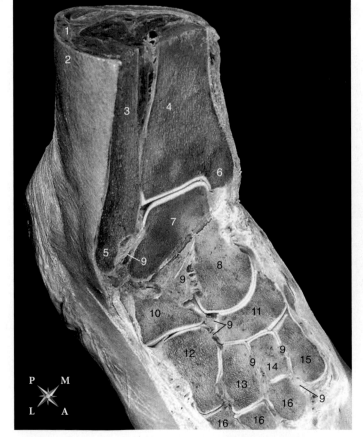

1 Superficial fascia
2 Skin
3 Fibula
4 Tibia
5 Lateral malleolus of fibula
6 Medial malleolus of tibia
7 Trochlea of talus
8 Head of talus
9 Interosseus ligaments
10 Calcaneous
11 Navicular
12 Cuboid
13 Third cuneiform
14 Second cuneiform
15 First cuneiform
16 Base of metatarsal

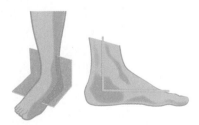

Figure 4-16 *Ankle and foot.* Combined cross section through anterior part of tarsal region and frontal (coronal) section through the lower leg and tarsal region.

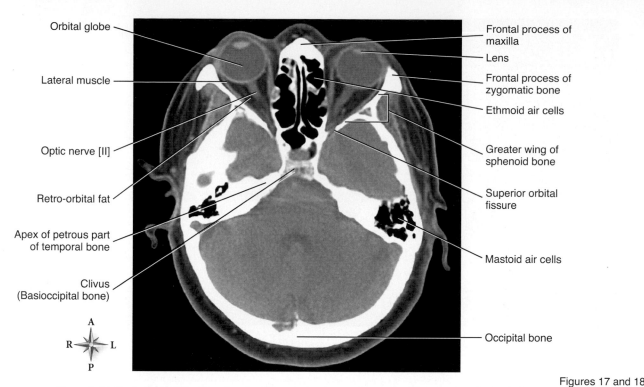

Orbital globe

Lateral muscle

Optic nerve [II]

Retro-orbital fat

Apex of petrous part of temporal bone

Clivus (Basioccipital bone)

Frontal process of maxilla

Lens

Frontal process of zygomatic bone

Ethmoid air cells

Greater wing of sphenoid bone

Superior orbital fissure

Mastoid air cells

Occipital bone

A
R — L
P

Figure 4-17 *Head.* Computerized tomography (CT) scan showing a cross section of the head at the level of the eye orbit.

Figures 17 and 18

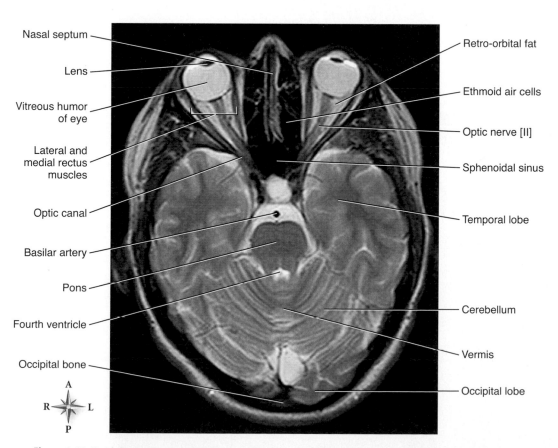

Nasal septum

Lens

Vitreous humor of eye

Lateral and medial rectus muscles

Optic canal

Basilar artery

Pons

Fourth ventricle

Occipital bone

Retro-orbital fat

Ethmoid air cells

Optic nerve [II]

Sphenoidal sinus

Temporal lobe

Cerebellum

Vermis

Occipital lobe

A
R — L
P

Figure 4-18 *Head.* Magnetic resonance imaging (MRI) scan showing a cross section of the head at the level of the eye orbit. Compare the similar cross section above (Figure 4-17) and note that visualization of individual structures varies depending on the imaging technology used to produce the image. (See ***Medical Imaging of the Body*** online at ***A&P Connect***.)

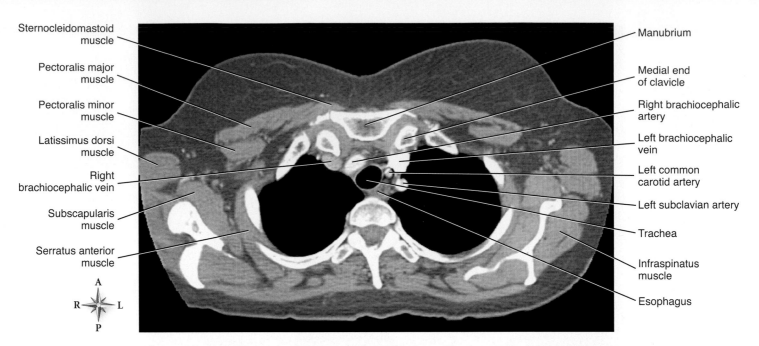

Sternocleidomastoid muscle

Pectoralis major muscle

Pectoralis minor muscle

Latissimus dorsi muscle

Right brachiocephalic vein

Subscapularis muscle

Serratus anterior muscle

Manubrium

Medial end of clavicle

Right brachiocephalic artery

Left brachiocephalic vein

Left common carotid artery

Left subclavian artery

Trachea

Infraspinatus muscle

Esophagus

Figure 4-19 *Thorax.* CT scan showing a cross section of the chest wall and structures of the mediastinum.

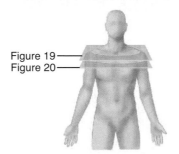

Figure 19

Figure 20

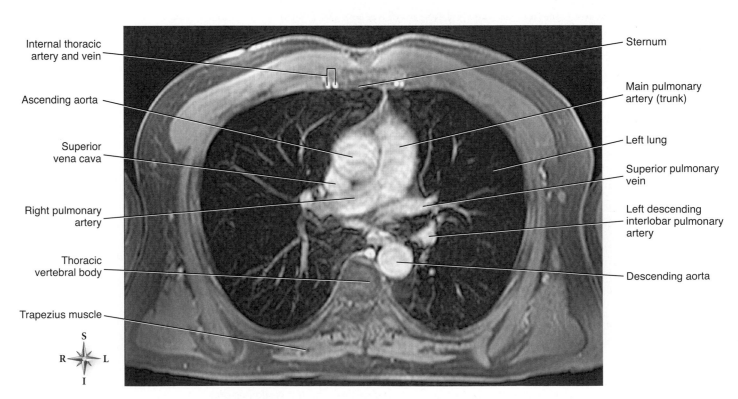

Internal thoracic artery and vein

Ascending aorta

Superior vena cava

Right pulmonary artery

Thoracic vertebral body

Trapezius muscle

Sternum

Main pulmonary artery (trunk)

Left lung

Superior pulmonary vein

Left descending interlobar pulmonary artery

Descending aorta

Figure 4-20 *Thorax.* MRI scan showing a cross section of the chest.

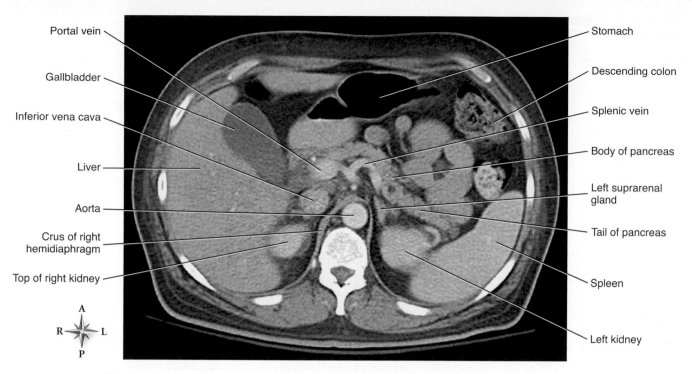

Portal vein

Gallbladder

Inferior vena cava

Liver

Aorta

Crus of right
hemidiaphragm

Top of right kidney

Stomach

Descending colon

Splenic vein

Body of pancreas

Left suprarenal
gland

Tail of pancreas

Spleen

Left kidney

A
R — L
P

Figure 4-21 *Abdomen.* CT scan showing a cross section of the upper abdominal wall and internal abdominal
organs.

Figure 21
Figure 22

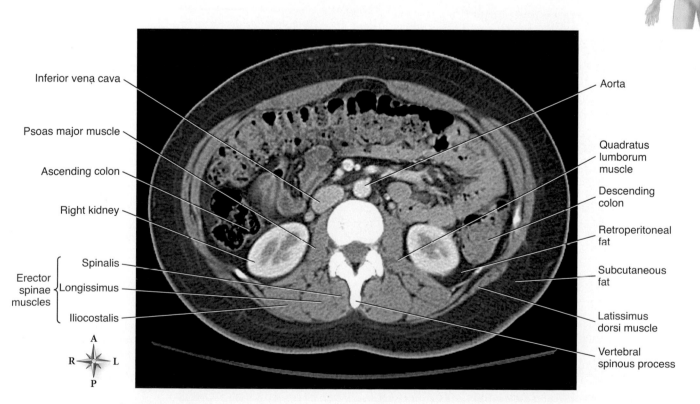

Inferior vena cava

Psoas major muscle

Ascending colon

Right kidney

Erector
spinae
muscles
{ Spinalis

Longissimus

Iliocostalis

Aorta

Quadratus
lumborum
muscle

Descending
colon

Retroperitoneal
fat

Subcutaneous
fat

Latissimus
dorsi muscle

Vertebral
spinous process

A
R — L
P

Figure 4-22 *Abdomen.* CT scan showing a cross section of the lower abdominal contents and wall. Note the
clear definition of the muscles of the back.

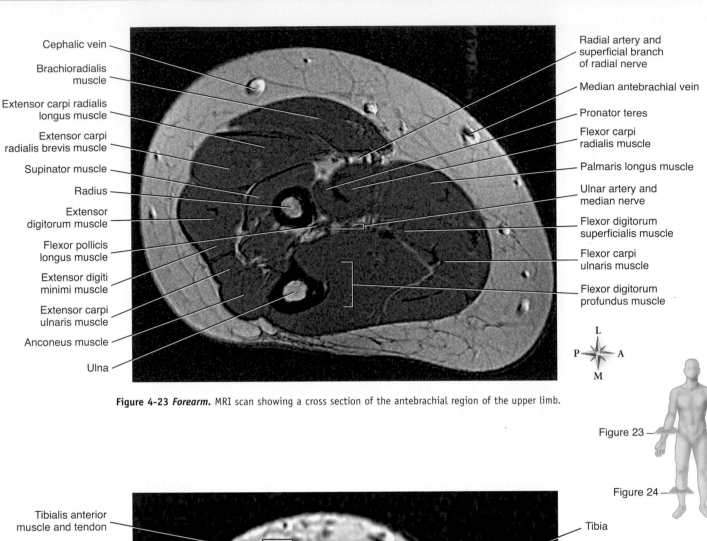

Cephalic vein

Brachioradialis muscle

Extensor carpi radialis longus muscle

Extensor carpi radialis brevis muscle

Supinator muscle

Radius

Extensor digitorum muscle

Flexor pollicis longus muscle

Extensor digiti minimi muscle

Extensor carpi ulnaris muscle

Anconeus muscle

Ulna

Radial artery and superficial branch of radial nerve

Median antebrachial vein

Pronator teres

Flexor carpi radialis muscle

Palmaris longus muscle

Ulnar artery and median nerve

Flexor digitorum superficialis muscle

Flexor carpi ulnaris muscle

Flexor digitorum profundus muscle

Figure 23

Figure 24

Figure 4-23 *Forearm.* MRI scan showing a cross section of the antebrachial region of the upper limb.

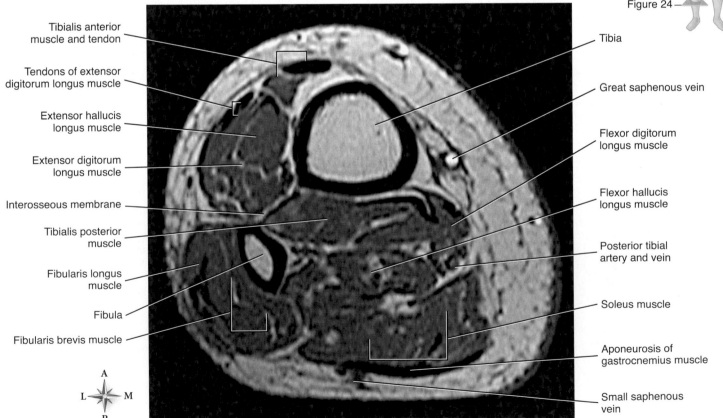

Tibialis anterior muscle and tendon

Tendons of extensor digitorum longus muscle

Extensor hallucis longus muscle

Extensor digitorum longus muscle

Interosseous membrane

Tibialis posterior muscle

Fibularis longus muscle

Fibula

Fibularis brevis muscle

Tibia

Great saphenous vein

Flexor digitorum longus muscle

Flexor hallucis longus muscle

Posterior tibial artery and vein

Soleus muscle

Aponeurosis of gastrocnemius muscle

Small saphenous vein

Figure 4-24 *Leg.* MRI scan showing a cross section near the calf of the leg.

Histology

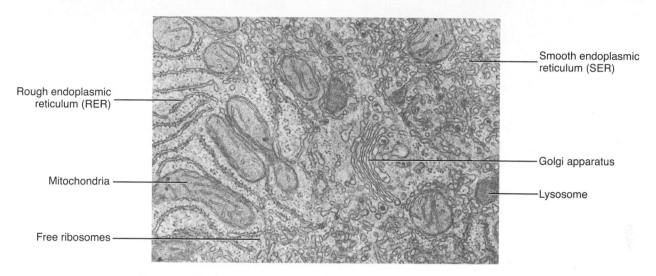

Figure 5-1 *Electron micrograph of a thin section of a liver cell showing organelles.*

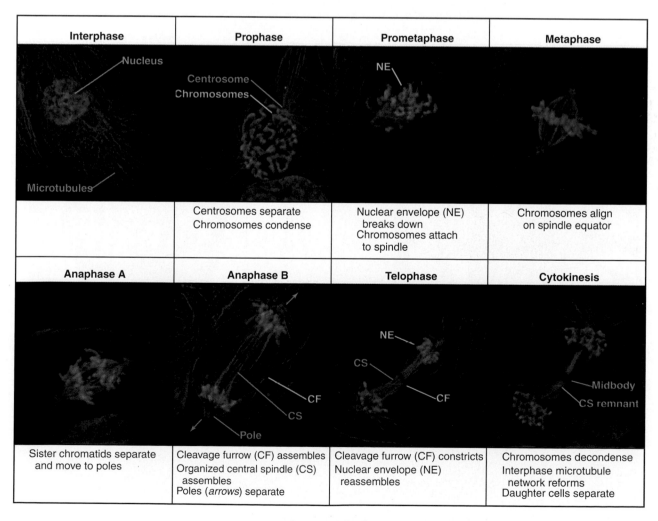

Figure 5-2 *Mitosis.*

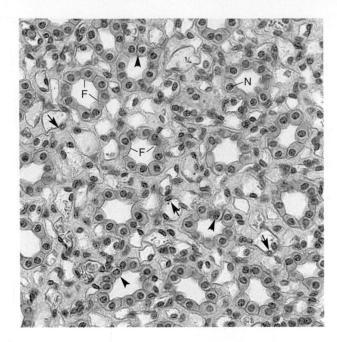

Figure 5-3 *Simple squamous epithelium* **(arrows)** *and simple cuboidal epithelium* **(arrowheads)** (×270). *F,* Free edge; *N,* nucleus.

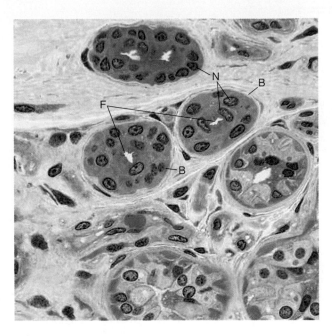

Figure 5-4 *Stratified cuboidal epithelium* (×509). *B,* Basement membrane; *F,* free edge; *N,* nucleus.

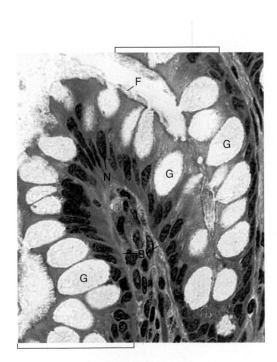

Figure 5-5 *Simple columnar epithelium with goblet cells* (×540). *G,* Goblet cell; *N,* nucleus; *B,* basement membrane; *F,* free edge.

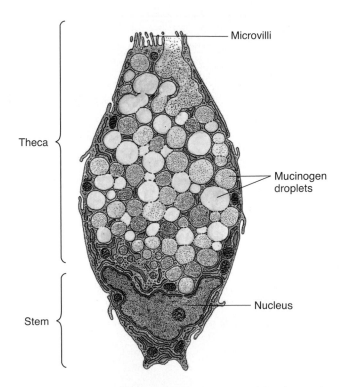

Figure 5-6 *Drawing of a goblet cell.* Schematic diagram of the ultrastructure of a goblet cell illustrating the tightly packed secretory granules of the theca.

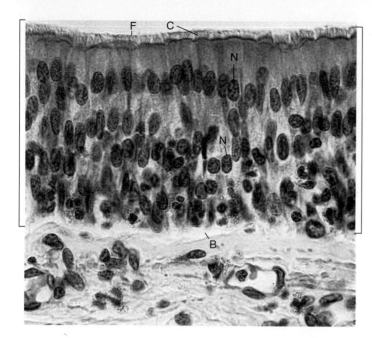

Figure 5-7 *Pseudostratified columnar epithelium* (×540). *B,* Basement membrane; *C,* cilia; *F,* free edge; *N,* nucleus.

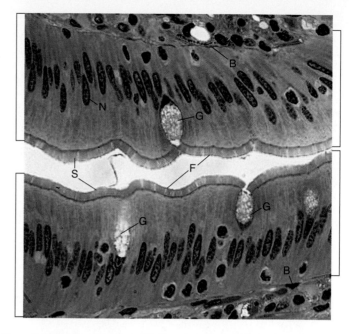

Figure 5-8 *Simple columnar epithelium* (×540). *G,* Goblet cell; *S,* striated border; *N,* nucleus; *F,* free edge; *B,* basement membrane.

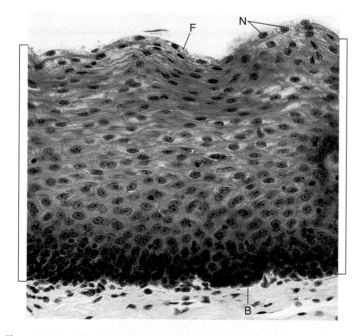

Figure 5-9 *Stratified squamous epithelium (nonkeratinized)* (×509). *B,* Basement membrane; *F,* free edge; *N,* nucleus.

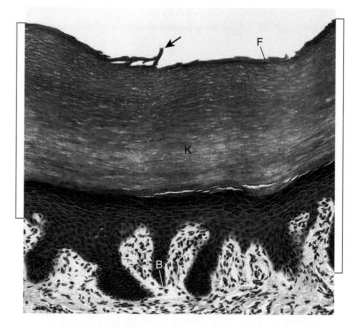

Figure 5-10 *Stratified squamous epithelium (keratinized)* (×125). *Arrow,* Flaking off of dead cells; *K,* keratinized layer; *F,* free edge; *B,* basement membrane.

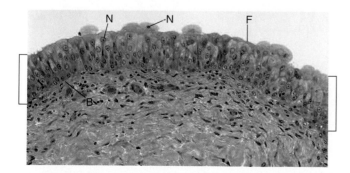

Figure 5-11 *Transitional epithelium* (×125). *B,* Basement membrane; *F,* free edge; *N,* nucleus.

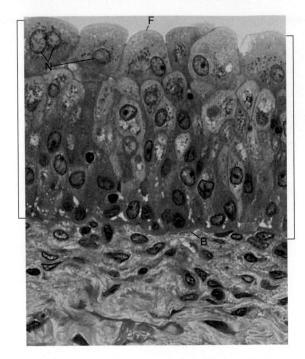

Figure 5-12 *Transitional epithelium* (×540). *B,* Basement membrane; *F,* free edge; *N,* nucleus.

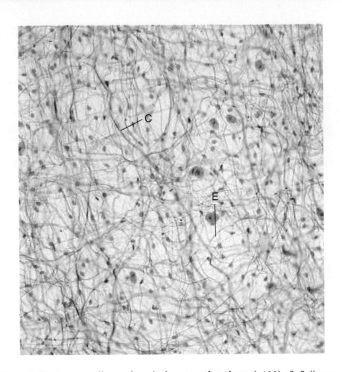

Figure 5-13 *Loose, ordinary (areolar) connective tissue* (×132). *C,* Collagen fiber; *E,* elastin fiber.

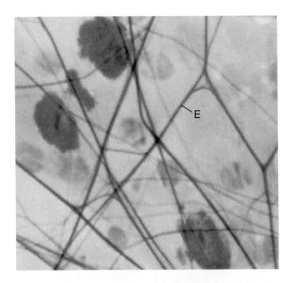

Figure 5-14 *Loose, ordinary (areolar) connective tissue* (high power). *E,* Elastin fiber.

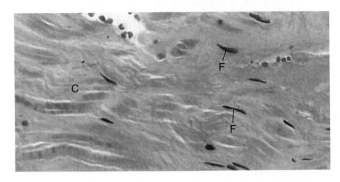

Figure 5-16 *Dense fibrous connective tissue.* *C,* Bundles of collagen fibers; *F,* fibroblasts.

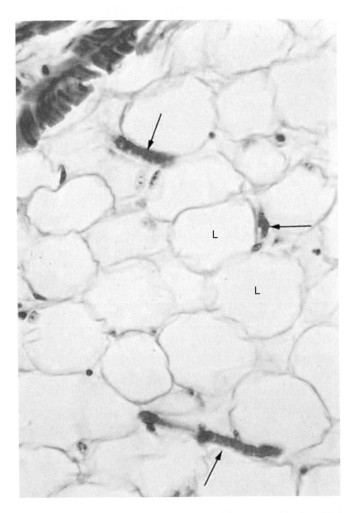

Figure 5-15 *Adipose tissue.* *L,* Lipid-storing vesicles; *arrows,* blood capillaries.

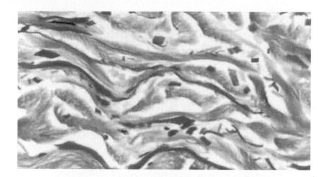

Figure 5-17 *Elastic fibrous connective tissue.*

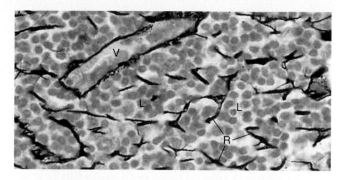

Figure 5-18 *Reticular connective tissue. L,* Lymphoid cells; *R,* reticular fibers; *V,* blood vessel.

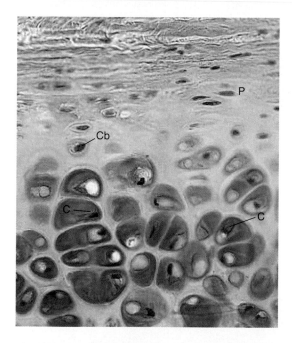

Figure 5-19 *Hyaline cartilage* (×270). *C,* Chondrocyte within a lacuna; *Cb,* chondroblast; *P,* perichondrium.

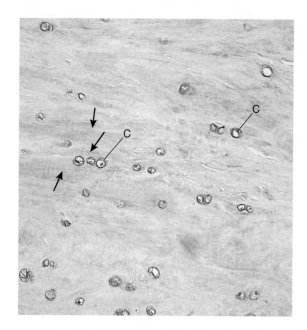

Figure 5-20 *Fibrocartilage* (×132). *C,* Chondrocyte in a lacuna; *arrow,* collagen fiber bundle.

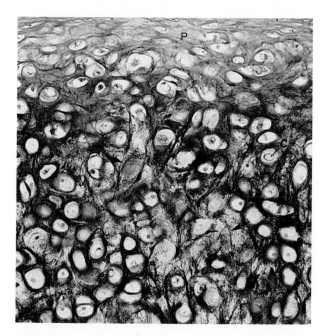

Figure 5-21 *Elastic cartilage* (×132). *P,* Perichondrium; *C,* chondrocyte in a lacuna; *arrow,* elastic fiber.

Figure 5-22 *Compact bone* (×270). *C,* Central (haversian) canal; *arrow,* canaliculus.

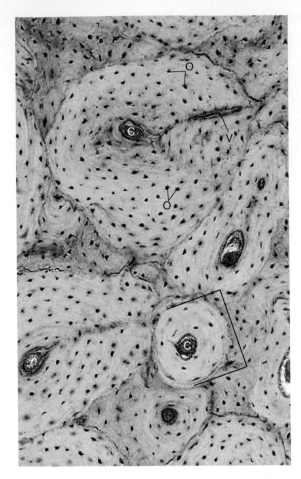

Figure 5-23 *Compact bone (decalcified)* (×162). *V,* Volkmann's canal; *C,* central canal; *O,* osteocyte; *bracket,* osteon (haversian system).

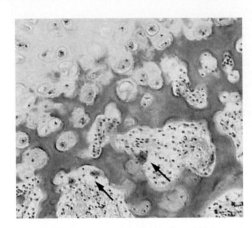

Figure 5-24 *Spongy (cancellous) bone tissue* (high power). *Arrows,* Osteoclasts.

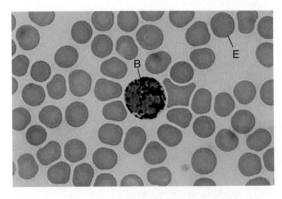

Figure 5-26 *Blood (smear showing basophil)* (×1325). *E,* Erythrocyte; *B,* basophil.

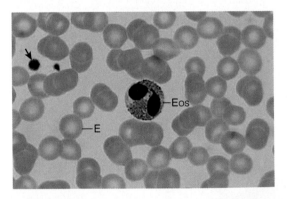

Figure 5-27 *Blood (smear showing eosinophil)* (×1325). *E,* Erythrocyte; *Eos,* eosinophil; *arrow,* platelet.

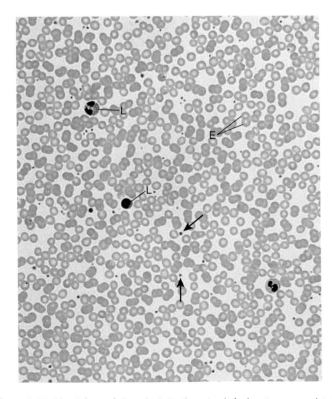

Figure 5-25 *Blood (smear)* (×270). *E,* Erythrocyte; *L,* leukocyte; *arrow,* platelet.

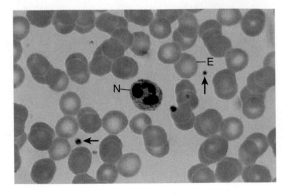

Figure 5-28 *Blood (smear showing neutrophil)* (×1325). *E,* Erythrocyte; *arrow,* platelet; *N,* neutrophil.

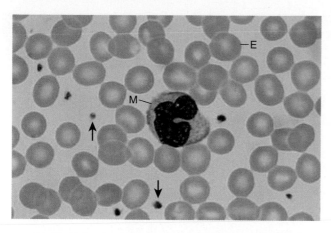

Figure 5-29 *Blood (smear showing monocyte)* (×1325). *E,* Erythrocyte; *M,* monocyte; *arrow,* platelet.

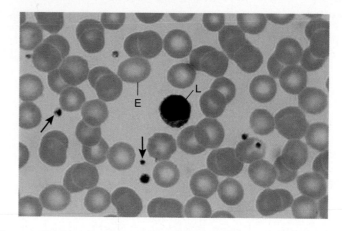

Figure 5-30 *Blood (smear showing lymphocyte)* (×1325). *E,* Erythrocyte; *arrow,* platelet; *L,* lymphocyte.

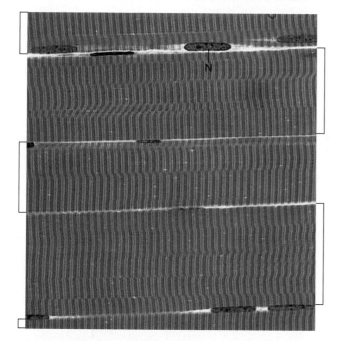

Figure 5-31 *Skeletal muscle (longitudinal section)* (×540). *N,* Nucleus.

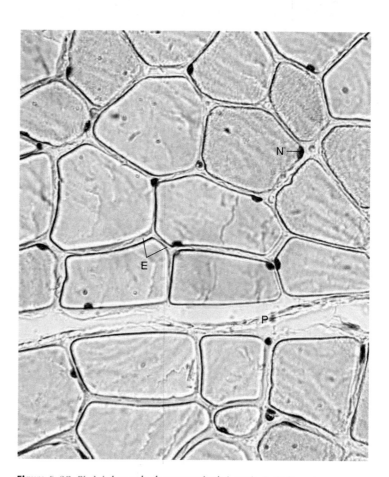

Figure 5-32 *Skeletal muscle (cross section)* (×540). *E,* Endomysium; *N,* nucleus; *P,* perimysium.

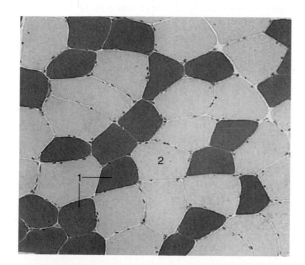

Figure 5-33 *Skeletal muscle (cross section).* *1,* Type 1 fibers; *2,* type 2 fibers.

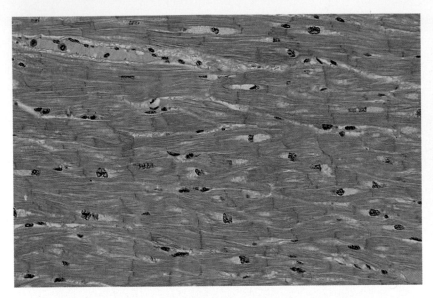

Figure 5-34 *Cardiac muscle showing branching (longitudinal section)* (×270).

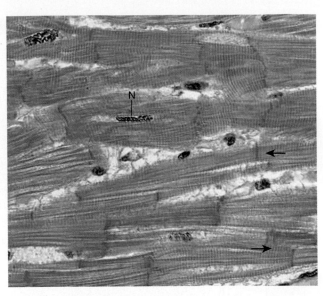

Figure 5-35 *Cardiac muscle (longitudinal section)* (×540). *N,* nucleus; *arrow,* intercalated disk.

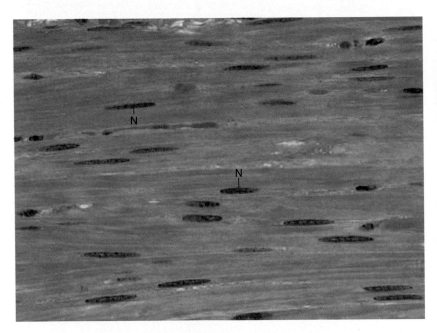

Figure 5-36 *Smooth muscle (longitudinal section)* (×540). *N,* Nucleus.

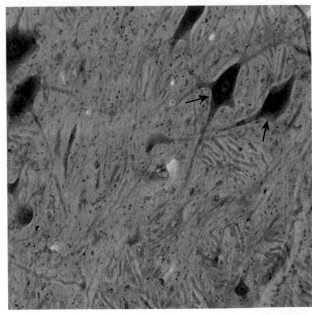

Figure 5-37 *Nerve tissue (spinal cord gray matter)* (×270). *Arrow,* Neuron.

Figure 5-38 *Nerve tissue (spinal cord smear).* *M,* Multipolar neuron; *N,* nuclei of glial cells.

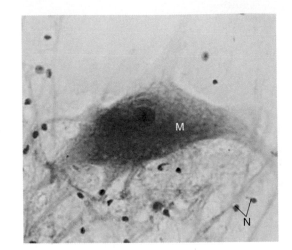

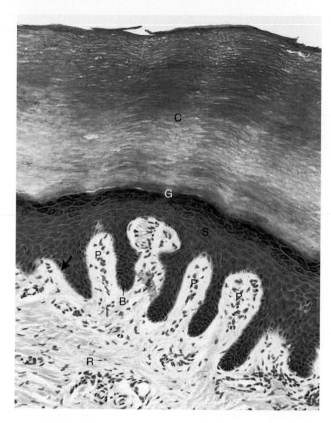

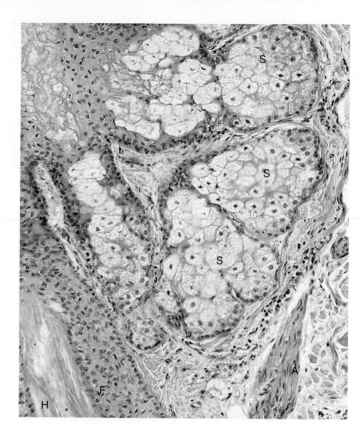

Figure 5-39 *Skin (thick)* (×132). Epidermis: *C,* Stratum corneum; *G,* stratum granulosum; *S,* stratum spinosum; *B,* stratum basale; *arrow,* dermal-epidermal junction. Dermis: *P,* Papilla (papillary region); *R,* reticular region.

Figure 5-40 *Sebaceous gland* (×132). *S,* Sebaceous gland; *A,* arrector pili muscle; *H,* hair; *F,* hair follicle.

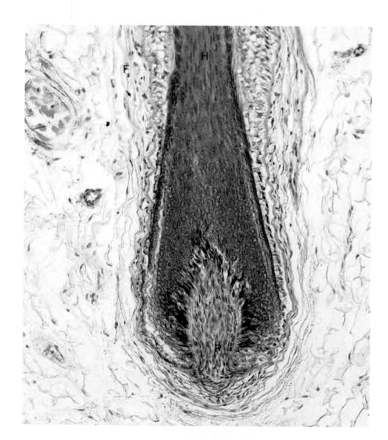

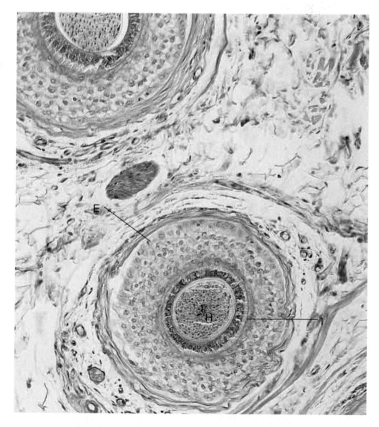

Figure 5-41 *Hair follicle (longitudinal section)* (×132). *F,* Follicle; *H,* hair; *P,* hair papilla.

Figure 5-42 *Hair follicle (cross section)* (×132). *E,* External root sheath; *I,* internal root sheath; *H,* hair.

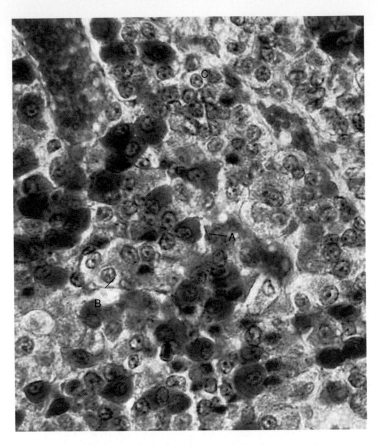

Figure 5-43 *Figure 5-43 Pituitary gland (anterior)* (×470). *A,* Acidophil; *B,* basophil; *C,* chromophil.

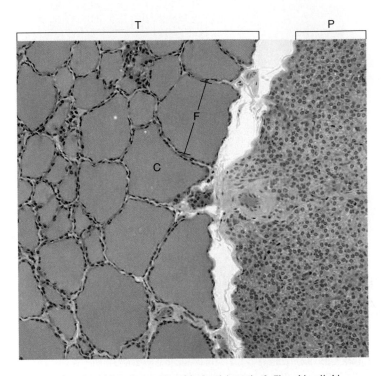

Figure 5-44 *Thyroid and parathyroid gland* (×132). *C,* Thyroid colloid; *F,* thyroid follicle; *P,* parathyroid gland; *T,* thyroid gland.

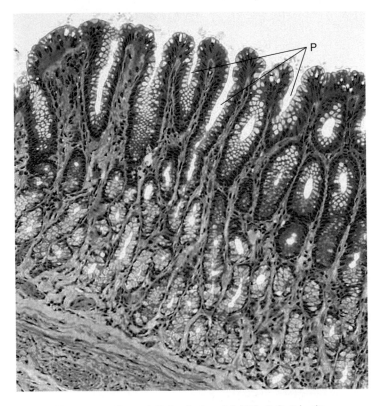

Figure 5-45 *Stomach lining (pylorus)* (×132). *P,* Gastric pits.

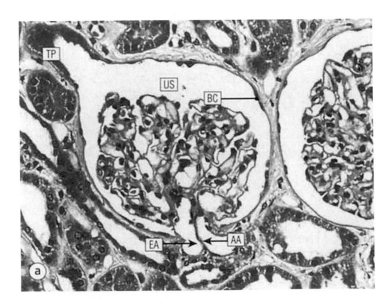

Figure 5-46 *Renal corpuscle of kidney.* *AA,* Afferent arteriole; *EA,* efferent arteriole; *TP,* proximal tubule; *US,* urinary space of Bowman's capsule; *BC,* parietal wall of Bowman's capsule.

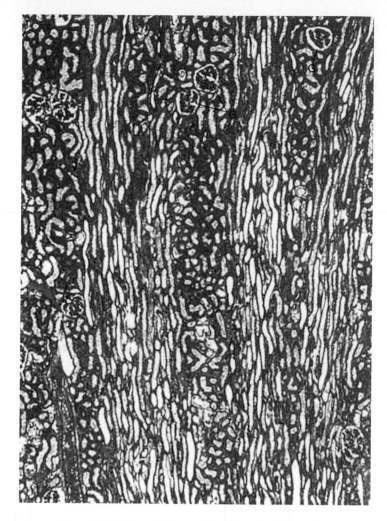

Figure 5-47 *Kidney tubules and blood vessels.* G, Glomerulus.

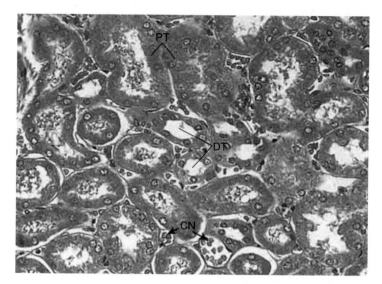

Figure 5-48 *Kidney tubules (cross section).* PT, Proximal tubule; DT, distal tubule; CN, capillary network.

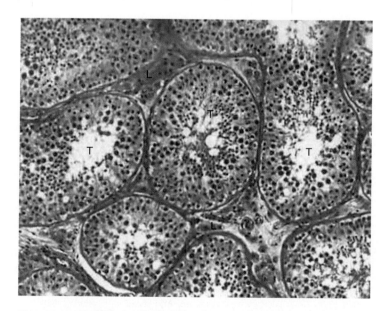

Figure 5-49 *Seminiferous tubules of testis (cross section).* T, Seminiferous tubule; L, interstitial (Leydig) cells.

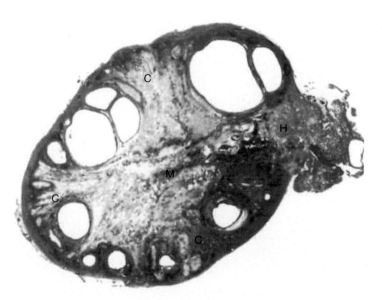

Figure 5-50 *Ovary (cross section).* H, Hilum; C, cortex; M, medulla.

Photograph/Illustration Credits

PART 1

Figures 1-1 to 1-36: Drake RL: *Gray's atlas of anatomy*, New York, 2008, Elsevier.

PART 2

Figures 2-1 to 2-11: Abrahams PH: *McMinn's color atlas of human anatomy*, ed 5, Philadelphia, 2003, Elsevier.

Figures 2-12 to 2-91: Muscolino JE: *Kinesiology: the skeletal system and muscle function*, St Louis, 2006, Elsevier.

PART 3

Figures 3-1 to 3-22: Abrahams PH: *McMinn's color atlas of human anatomy*, ed 5, Philadelphia, 2003, Elsevier.

PART 4

Figures 4-1 to 4-8: Abrahams PH: *McMinn's color atlas of human anatomy*, ed 5, Philadelphia, 2003, Elsevier.

Figures 4-9 to 4-16: Gosling JA: *Human anatomy color atlas and text*, ed 4, London, 2002, Elsevier.

Figures 4-17 to 4-24: Moses K: *Atlas of clinical gross anatomy*, Edinburgh, 2005, Elsevier.

PART 5

Figure 5-1: Courtesy Don Fawcett, Harvard Medical School.

Figure 5-2: Pollard TD, Earnshaw WC: *Cell biology*, Philadelphia, 2004, Elsevier.

Figures 5-3, 5-4, 5-5, 5-6, 5-7, 5-8, 5-9, 5-10, 5-11, 5-12, 5-13, 5-19, 5-20, 5-21, 5-22, 5-23, 5-25, 5-26, 5-27, 5-28, 5-29, 5-30, 5-31, 5-32, 5-34, 5-35, 5-36, 5-37, 5-39, 5-40, 5-41, 5-42, 5-43, 5-44, 5-45: Gartner LP, Hiatt JL: *Color textbook of histology*, ed 2, Burlington, 2001, Elsevier.

Figures 5-14, 5-15, 5-24, 5-38: Leeson TS, Leeson CR, Paparo AA: *Text/atlas of histology*, Philadelphia, 1988, Elsevier.

Figures 5-16, 5-17, 5-18, 5-33, 5-46, 5-47, 5-48, 5-49, 5-50: Stevens A, Lowe JS: *Human histology*, ed 3, Philadelphia, 2005, Elsevier.